Contents

List of figures

RethinkX Team

Authors

James Arbib and Tony Seba

Contributors

Richard Anderson (editor)

Adam Dorr (research fellow)

Taylor Hinds (research associate)

Bradd Libby (research fellow)

Catherine Tubb (research fellow)

Uzair Niazi (director)

Contact

RethinkX: info@rethinkx.com

Media: media@rethinkx.com

Follow us at:

/rethink_x

/JoinRethinkX

/company/rethinkx

We invite you to join our community. To learn more, please visit www.rethinkx.com

With Thanks

Morry Cater and the team at Cater Communications, and the design team at Lokate Design, particularly Jack Hagley.

Thanks also to John Elkington, Paul Gilding, Guido Jouret, and Jose Cordeiro.

Our thanks in no way implies agreement with all (or any) of our assumptions and findings. Any mistakes are our own.

Introduction

Tony and I met at a military think-tank briefing to discuss the potential geopolitical implications of the disruption of energy and transportation.

Top mainstream analysts from major corporations, government, and NGOs discussed the apparently linear, incremental progress that solar, batteries, and electric vehicles were making and how "the transition" would take decades. The two of us, both independent outsiders with no big institutions behind us, were dumbfounded. We shared a very different view – these were not transitions but technology disruptions. Technology disruptions are not linear progressions and they do not take decades to play out. They may appear to start slowly, but they move exponentially as they trigger powerful feedback mechanisms that drive extremely rapid change, the impacts of which can ripple out across not just the economy but society itself.

Chastened by the idea that investors, governments, businesses, and civic leaders were being fed such inaccurate and dangerously misleading analysis, we decided to set up our own think tank. RethinkX was thus born as an independent, not-for-profit research organization designed to provide leaders across society with better information on which to make decisions. We have since engaged with investors with trillions of dollars of assets under management including BlackRock, Goldman Sachs, J.P. Morgan, and sovereign wealth funds, as well as large businesses and governments around the world including China, the EU, and states throughout the U.S. The South Korean military alone bought more than 9,000 copies of Tony's Amazon best-selling book *Clean Disruption*, and our work has been featured in numerous documentaries and news shows.

Our work is based on a framework Tony created to analyze the complex processes that drive a pattern of rapid, non-linear change and to anticipate technology-driven disruptions and their implications. Our predictions are very different from those of mainstream analysts, who produce linear forecasts based on a mechanistic and siloed ('simple systems') methodology that does not account for the fact that sectors of the economy and, indeed, society are complex, adaptive systems. This leads them to underestimate improvements in the cost and capabilities of technologies, the speed of their adoption, and the rapid speed of collapse of incumbents, all the while ignoring the broader implications of disruption.

We have been consistently more accurate than others in predicting the speed and scale of technological disruption:

- In 2010, Tony forecast that, by 2020, the cost of generating solar PV energy would drop to 3-5 cents/kWh (at the time the cost was 15 cents/kWh). The cost today is less than 4 cents/kWh. Mainstream analysts were far more conservative. The same year, the International Energy Agency, for example, forecast a cost of 7 cents/kWh by 2030.
- In 2010, Tony forecast that, by 2020, the cost of lithium-ion batteries would drop to $200/kWh or below (the cost at the time was $1,100/kWh). Today, they cost around $150/kWh. Again, mainstream analysts were not even close – in 2013, for example, the consultant PWC forecast a cost of $300 in 2020.
- In 2014, *Clean Disruption* forecast the dramatic disruption of the energy sector with serious knock-on effects, all of which have come to pass, including the collapse of the coal industry (the Dow Jones Coal Index has since fallen by 96%), as well as the end of natural gas peaker plants. No-one else has predicted this speed or scale of change in the energy sector.
- Also in *Clean Disruption*, Tony forecast that the cost of a 200-mile range electric vehicle (EV) would fall to $30,000 by 2020 (the cost at the time was $70,000) – below the average price of a new gasoline vehicle in America. Today, a GWM Ora R1 EV in China costs around $20,000.
- In 2017, RethinkX predicted that oil demand would peak at 100 million barrels a day by 2020 and the collapse of oil prices would be felt as early as 2021. This is happening now. No-one else foresaw this. We also predicted that demand would drop by 30 million barrels a day by 2030. Mainstream analysts, industry experts, and insiders did not see this happening until the 2040s or 2050s at the earliest. It has already happened.
- In 2017, when mainstream analysts were forecasting that the world's car fleet would double over the next two decades, we forecast that new internal combustion engine vehicle peak sales would happen by 2020. They peaked in 2019. We forecast that car resale values would plunge to zero or even turn negative. This fall is happening now. We forecast that the EV industry would develop one million-mile EV powertrains in the 2020s. Several car companies have already announced them.

» In 2017, we calculated that autonomous technology could be five times safer than human drivers by 2020 and ten times safer by 2022. Tesla's data indicate their EVs with Autopilot engaged are now between six and nine times safer than the average human-driven car in America.

To demonstrate the power of his framework and methodology, in 2005 Tony put together a virtual stock portfolio of 15 companies inventing and implementing disruptive products, platforms, and business models. As of February 2020, the portfolio had risen by 2,500%, or 25% a year, massively outperforming the market – over the same period, the Dow Jones Industrial Average rose 296% (10% a year) while the Nasdaq rose 437% (12% a year). The average U.S. equity fund returned 180% (7% a year).

To date, our work has focused on individual sector disruptions. In 2017, we published *Rethinking Transportation 2020-2030*, which predicted that technological and business model convergence would result in a 10x improvement in costs and capabilities of new technologies, disrupting transportation as soon as 2021. As a result, by 2030 95% of all U.S. passenger miles traveled would be served by on-demand, autonomous, electric vehicles owned by fleets. We call the new business model Transportation-as-a-Service (TaaS). The impacts of TaaS include an 80% reduction in transportation energy demand, a 90% reduction in tailpipe emissions, $1 trillion in household savings, and more than 200 million cars taken off American roads.

In 2019, we published *Rethinking Food and Agriculture 2020-2030*, applying the same analysis and modeling to the industrial agriculture sector. We found that, due to rapid improvement in the cost and capabilities of technologies like precision fermentation, genome sequencing, and CRISPR, and a new model of production we call Food-as-Software, the cost of proteins would be 10x cheaper than existing animal proteins by 2035, while the number of cows in the U.S. would have fallen by 50% and the cattle farming industry would effectively be bankrupt by 2030.

Our research for this book revealed that our framework could be extended to explain society as a whole, across the past, present, and future. For the same processes and dynamics that drive S-curve adoption of new products at a sector level repeat at the level of civilizations.

The timing of publication is no coincidence. Today, the five foundational sectors of the global economy – information, energy, transport, food, and materials – are being disrupted at an unprecedented speed and scale. The implications for the wider economy, societies, and indeed our civilization itself are profound. Indeed the 2020s will be the most disruptive decade in history. Covid-19 has simply pulled the curtain on the fragility of current models of production and governance. It is just one of a series of predictable shocks that threaten to devastate our civilization if, collectively, we do not make the right choices.

Rethinking Humanity, therefore, is a clarion call to leaders across society – public and private – to see what is really happening, to understand the implications, and to redefine the way we all do business, invest, and organize society. We publish the book as a free beta version to introduce these ideas and concepts in the hope that we can kickstart discussions across society and inspire others to join us in further developing and implementing the thesis and the evidence base. In doing so, we hope to focus attention on choices that can help lead to a more equitable, healthy, resilient, and stable society.

James Arbib

Executive Summary

We are on the cusp of the fastest, deepest, most consequential transformation of human civilization in history, a transformation every bit as significant as the move from foraging to cities and agriculture 10,000 years ago.

During the 2020s, key technologies will converge to completely disrupt the five foundational sectors that underpin the global economy, and with them every major industry in the world today. The knock-on effects for society will be as profound as the extraordinary possibilities that emerge.

In information, energy, food, transportation, and materials, costs will fall by 10x or more, while production processes an order of magnitude (10x) more efficient will use 90% fewer natural resources with 10x-100x less waste. The prevailing production system will shift away from a model of centralized extraction and the breakdown of scarce resources that requires vast physical scale and reach, to a model of localized creation from limitless, ubiquitous building blocks – a world built not on coal, oil, steel, livestock, and concrete but on photons, electrons, DNA, molecules and (q)bits. Product design and development will be performed collaboratively over information networks while physical production and distribution will be fulfilled locally. As a result, geographic advantage will be eliminated as every city or region becomes self-sufficient. This new creation-based production system, which will be built on technologies we are already using today, will be far more equitable, robust, and resilient than any we have ever seen. We have the opportunity to move from a world of extraction to one of creation, a world of scarcity to one of plenitude, a world of inequity and predatory competition to one of shared prosperity and collaboration.

This is not, then, another Industrial Revolution, but a far more fundamental shift. This is the beginning of the third age of humankind – the Age of Freedom.

The possibilities that open up in this new age are truly extraordinary. Within 10-15 years, everyone on the planet could have access to the 'American Dream' for a few hundred dollars a month. For the first time in history, poverty could be overcome easily. Access to all our basic needs – food, energy, transportation, information, and shelter – could become a fundamental human right. Armed conflict, often driven by the need to access and control scarce resources, could become largely unnecessary. Climate change and environmental degradation, caused by production processes that take no account of the destruction they wreak on the natural world, could be overcome by a new production system delivering zero-carbon energy, transportation, and food with marginal waste. This could allow us to restore the integrity of the planet's natural systems and help mitigate the impact of our unsustainable actions on human health. We may, ultimately, be able to escape toil and drudgery entirely and, for the first time in history, achieve real freedom – the freedom to spend our time creatively, unburdened by financial precariousness and the need to provide for ourselves and our families. Never before has humanity seen such an astonishing array of possibilities opened up in such a short period of time.

But this future is by no means predetermined. Indeed it cannot be achieved by technological progress alone.

History indicates that leading civilizations have evolved ever-greater organizational capabilities in tandem with increased technological capabilities. While the technological capabilities dictate the potential of any civilization, the Organizing System determines how close to this potential a society can get. The Organizing System encompasses both the fundamental beliefs, institutions, and reward systems that enable optimal decisions to be taken across a society, and the structures that manage, control, govern, and influence its population. The best combination of technology and Organizing System that is available dictates the winners – for example a city of 10,000 people, such as Sumer, requires a very different Organizing System from one of a million people, such as Rome.

Throughout history, 10x advancements in the five foundational sectors have driven the emergence of a new and vastly more capable civilization than any which has come before. But this has only been possible when combined with vastly improved organizational capabilities. This has always represented a formidable challenge for incumbents, and the lessons of history are sobering – every leading civilization, from Çatalhöyük and Sumer to Babylonia and Rome, has fallen as it reached the limits of its ability to organize society and solve the problems created by its production system. When these civilizations were threatened with collapse, they looked backwards and attempted to recapture the glory days by patching up their production system and doubling down on their Organizing System rather than adapting. The result was descent into a dark age.

Today, our incumbent leadership in government and industry are making the same mistake. The patterns of history are clear. The five foundational sectors, which gave rise to Western dominance starting with Europe in the 1500s and America in the 1900s, will all collapse during the 2020s. These sector disruptions are bookends to a civilization that birthed the Industrial Order, which both built the modern world and destroyed the rest. Furthermore, we are experiencing rising inequality, extremism, and populism, the deterioration of decision-making processes and the undermining of representative democracy, the accumulation of financial instability as we mortgage the future to pay for the present, ecological degradation, and climate change – all signs that our civilization has reached and breached its limits. The response from today's incumbents to these challenges – more centralization, more extraction, more exploitation, more compromise of public health and environmental integrity in the name of competitive advantage and growth – is no less desperate than the response from those of prior civilizations who called for more walls, more priests, and more blood sacrifices as they faced collapse.

And this is just the beginning – as new technologies develop apace, their disruptive power will only grow stronger. Ironically, the same technologies that hold the promise of solving our most pressing problems are also accelerating collapse, challenging the ability of our outdated and increasingly incompatible Organizing System to function.

Indeed we are already seeing the impact of the new, creation-based production system butting up against our increasingly antiquated Organizing System. The information sector, for example, has already been disrupted. Centralized content production with high costs, high barriers to entry, and narrow distribution channels has given way to billions of producer-consumers generating content at near-zero cost with minimal barriers to entry across a globally-connected network. Alongside the extraordinary benefits it has brought, this emerging production system has also created novel problems which our Organizing System is incapable of understanding or managing. A few computer hackers in an apartment in one country can hijack another's governance processes, spread false narratives, polarize public opinion, paralyze decision-making processes, and help enable regime change home and abroad. Individual nations are no longer able to manage the narrative or control the flow of information. The upcoming disruptions that will unfold simultaneously in the energy, food, transportation, and materials sectors during the 2020s will present further unprecedented new challenges at the same time as solving old problems.

The choice, therefore, is stark – collapse into a new dark age or move to a new Organizing System that allows us to flourish in a new Age of Freedom. Such a move will not be easy – we will need to rethink not just the structures and institutions that manage society, but the very concepts they are built on. Representative democracy, capitalism, and nation states may seem like fundamental truths but they are, in fact, merely human constructs that emerged and evolved in an industrial Organizing System. In the new age, they may well become redundant.

For the first time in history, we have not just the technological tools to make an incredible leap in societal capabilities, but the understanding and foresight to see what is coming. We have the choice, therefore, to avert disaster or not. We can choose to elevate humanity to new heights and use the upcoming convergence of technology disruptions to end poverty, inequality, resource conflict, and environmental destruction, all for a fraction of the cost we incur dealing with them today. Or we can choose to preserve the failing status quo and descend into another dark age like every leading civilization before us.

Dark ages do not occur for lack of sunshine, but for lack of leadership. The established centers of power, the U.S., Europe, or China, handicapped by incumbent mindsets, beliefs, interests, and institutions, are unlikely to lead. In a globally competitive world, smaller, hungrier, more adaptable communities, cities, or states such as Israel, Mumbai, Dubai, Singapore, Lagos, Shanghai, California, or Seattle are more likely to develop a winning Organizing System. They will appear, just like their predecessors, as if from nowhere, with capabilities far beyond those of incumbent leaders. Everyone else could get trampled before they have time to understand what is happening.

The intervening decade will be turbulent, destabilized both by technology disruptions that upend the foundations of the global economy and by system shocks from pandemics, geopolitical conflict, natural disasters, financial crises, and social unrest that could lead to dramatic tipping points for humanity including mass migrations and even war. In the face of each new crisis we will be tempted to look backward rather than forward, to mistake ideology and dogma for reason and wisdom, to turn on each other instead of trusting one another.

If we hold strong, we can emerge together to create the wealthiest, healthiest, most extraordinary civilization in history. If we do not, we will join the ranks of every other failed civilization for future historians to puzzle over. Our children will either thank us for bringing them an Age of Freedom, or curse us for condemning them to another dark age. The choice is ours.

Book Guide

This book is about the patterns and processes through human history that drive change within human-built, complex, adaptive systems.

It shows that key patterns recur across these systems, from individual industries disrupted over the course of just a few years by a single new technology, to entire civilizations becoming an order of magnitude more capable or collapsing as they reach their limits, both environmental and organizational. It includes a series of simplified framework boxes that apply these patterns to different parts of society.

Part 1: Begins with the process of change at the sector level with the arrival of the smartphone (information sector). It explores the process of disruption and shows how the impacts of technology convergence and exponential adoption within one sector of the economy ripple out across the whole of society. It then goes back to the 20th century and shows how the exact same patterns played out with the arrival of another disruptive product, this time the automobile (transport sector). Finally, it takes brief look at how the same process played out in the 15th century with even more profound consequences, when the printed book (information sector) sparked a transformation in our political, social, economic, and belief systems that fundamentally changed the entire world.

Part 2: Looks back at the history of civilizations to understand how the processes of change at a sector level are repeated in the rise and fall of civilizations, starting with the rise of cities and agriculture 10,000 years ago. Order-of-magnitude technological improvements in the five foundational sectors, combined with adaptations in organizational capabilities, have allowed civilizations to break through previous limits in societal capabilities. These civilizations have then expanded and overrun peoples with lower capabilities until they breached their own limits, before collapsing into a dark age. This cycle has been repeated throughout history.

Part 3: Argues that we are now, once again, reaching our limits and the context is set for collapse. At the same time, extraordinary technological progress in the foundational sectors is creating the possibility of breakthrough to a new Age of Freedom. But this progress will destabilize society further and breakthrough cannot happen within our existing Organizing System because the emerging system of production is fundamentally different to anything we have ever seen before. Not only is our existing Organizing System unable to understand, manage, or control this production system, which is based on creation and plenitude rather than extraction and scarcity, but the new production system is actively undermining our existing Organizing System and speeding up the process of collapse. Our misguided efforts to patch up our current Organizing System are simply accelerating this process further.

Part 4: Looks ahead to identify the two alternate pathways before us – breakthrough or collapse. We are in a unique position – for the first time in history, we have the opportunity to break through before we collapse. To reach the Age of Freedom, we must overcome a three-fold challenge. First, we must rethink the present and the future to appreciate what is happening in the world today and develop the tools to manage a new Organizing System better suited to the emerging system of production. Second, we must enable the future we want by creating the conditions in which this new Organizing System can emerge and flourish. And third, we must bridge the journey by protecting people, maintaining social stability, and selectively keeping portions of our current system functioning while the new system emerges.

Framework Box 1. Simplicity Underlying Complexity: Change in Complex Systems

Change in complex systems can be characterized by long periods of stability punctuated by short periods of rapid change. This pattern is seen in all complex systems, which include the human body, the economy, and ecosystems.

During periods of equilibrium, the system is dominated by self-correcting feedbacks (brakes) and adaptations that act as a constraint on change. Forces for change to the system are kept in check by these brakes and the system remains stable.

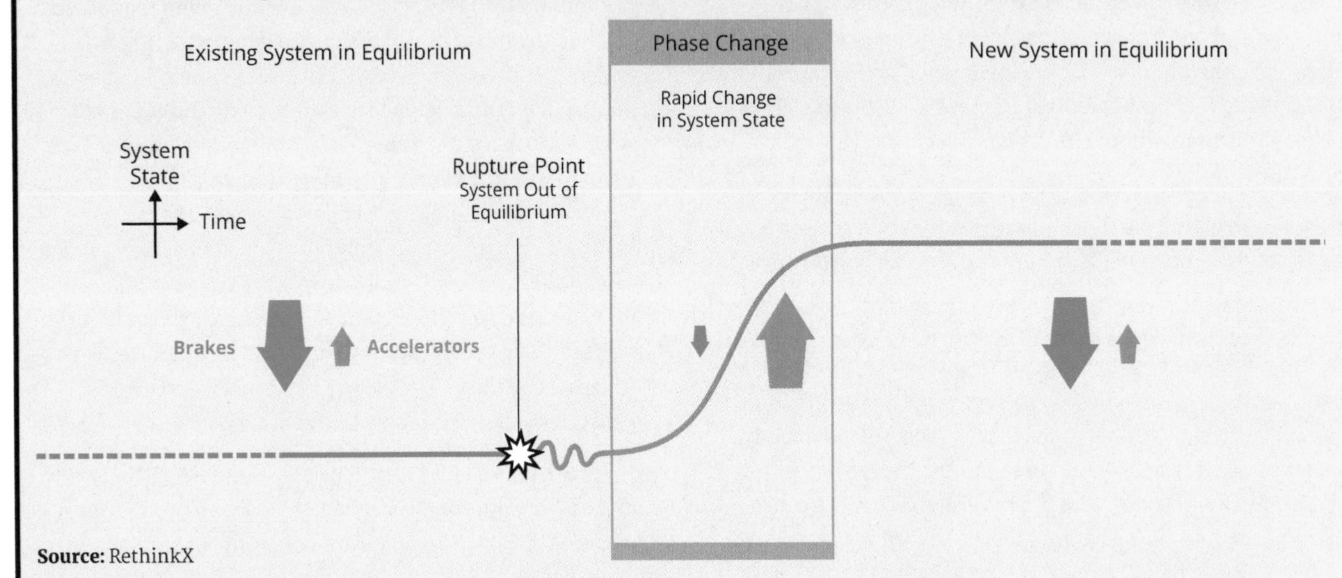

Source: RethinkX

Occasionally, a convergence of factors can amplify the forces for change, which then overpower the brakes. These self-reinforcing feedbacks (accelerators) can destabilize the system and push it out of equilibrium. The point at which the system moves out of equilibrium is the 'rupture point'. At this point, a change in system state is almost inevitable, as the accelerators drive rapid change and push the system into a new equilibrium. The rupture point sees an expansion of possible outcomes (a new possibility space). Thus, convergence leads to divergence. Continuation of the current state has a probability of almost zero, while a new state governed by different rules has a high probability.

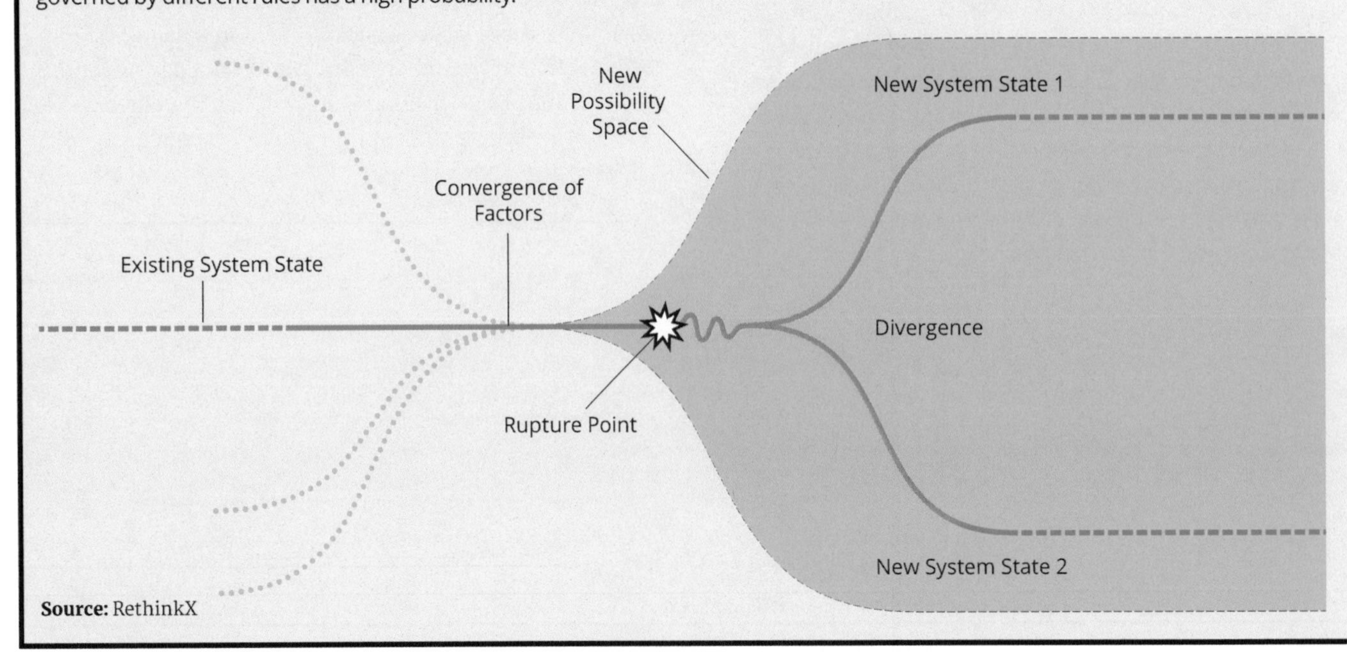

Source: RethinkX

This rapid change in system state is a 'phase change'. The impacts of this phase change ripple outwards and affect other connected systems, potentially causing them to rupture and change state too. The impacts of phase change in these connected systems can then ripple back and affect the process of change in the original system. While modeling complex systems is extremely difficult, there are often only a limited number of equilibrium states around which the possible outcomes of phase changes cluster.

These concepts can be illustrated through the example of disease.

The behavior of the human body is dominated by self-correcting feedback mechanisms that, among other things, hold the core temperature stable, maintain a stable blood glucose level, keep the blood oxygenated properly, and maintain the pH level. These processes help keep the body in a stable, healthy equilibrium state, or homeostasis.

At a cellular level, we can see cells change state without any effect on connected systems but, occasionally, we can see the impact of change cascade.

The Covid-19 virus, for example, can invade individual cells in the human body. In most people, this will trigger an immune response (a brake) that ultimately overcomes the virus with few or no serious symptoms. Occasionally, a convergence of factors leads these self-correcting processes to break down. Age, compromised immune response, and genetic predisposition, for example, can mean the body is unable to successfully fight back against the virus. As the virus spreads through the body, it can attack the function of cells in the lungs, causing cells to change state. Failure at cell level cascades across connected systems, causing failure at organ level as the lungs fail to function, ultimately causing death.

That individual is part of a community and broader society, and he or she affects and is affected by broader systems. The impact of the death of individuals changes the actions and decisions of other individuals across society as a whole, including economic, social, and political outcomes and decisions, potentially pushing these higher-level systems out of equilibrium and into new states.

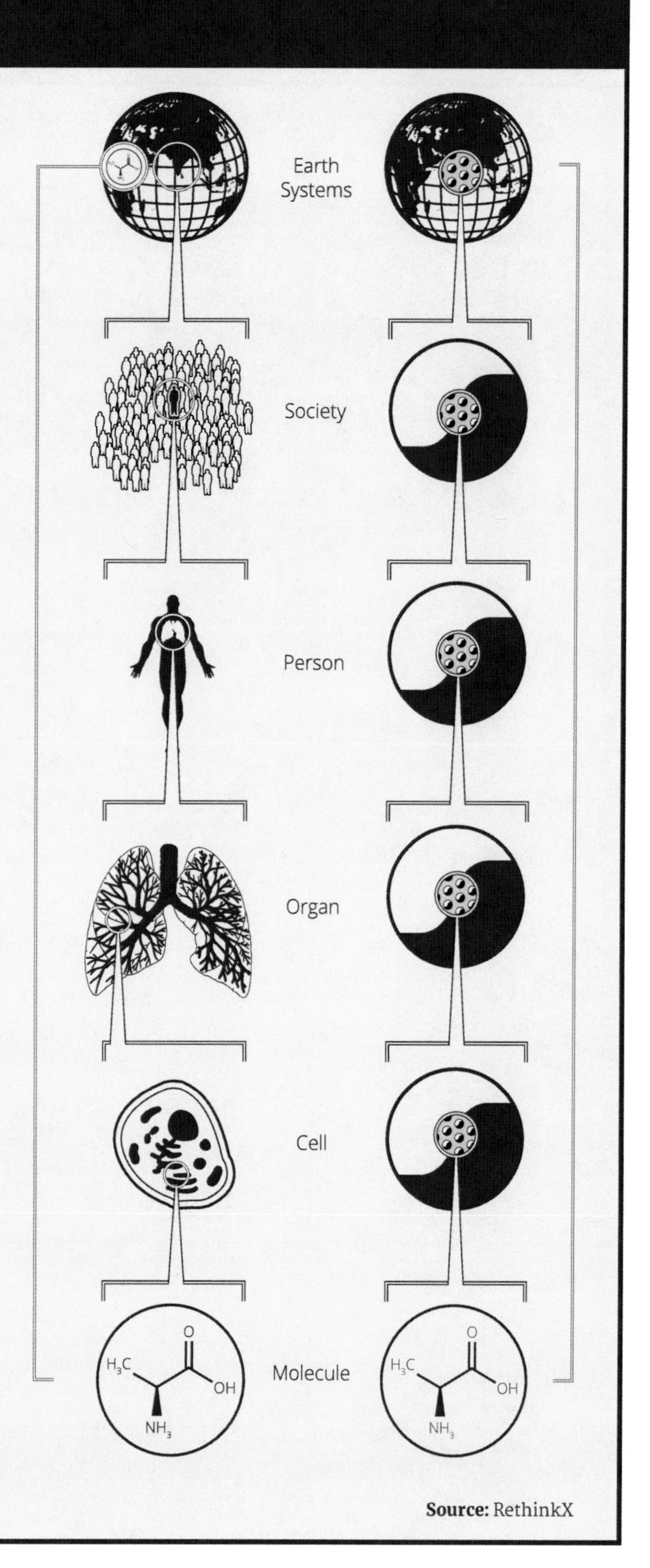

Source: RethinkX

Part 1

Rethinking Disruption: Technology Convergence and Organizing Systems Driving Societal Transformation

1.1 How the Smartphone Disrupted the Oil Industry

When Steve Jobs unveiled the very first iPhone at the San Francisco Macworld Convention in January 2007, the expectant crowd was full of techies, comms professionals, and the obligatory assortment of Apple devotees.

Oil executives were nowhere to be seen. For who could possibly have imagined the introduction of a new pocket-sized communications device represented an existential threat to the global oil industry?

But this is precisely what the smartphone has become. Understanding how and why is key to understanding disruption – how new technologies quickly take hold and impact not just the industry that developed them, but other sectors, the wider economy, and society itself.

Why, for example, did the iPhone appear in 2007? Why not 2005 or 2009? The answer is very simple – it was built on a series of underlying technologies, each of which needed to develop to the point where a $600 smartphone became possible. The cost and capabilities (size, weight, reliability, and functionality[1]) of each of these individual technologies needed to reach a level that, when combined, resulted in a product both good enough to satisfy consumers' desires and cheap enough they were prepared to buy it.

Technology Convergence

In the early 2000s, each of these technologies benefited from improvements made in different markets as increasing sales volumes, competition, and investment of capital and ingenuity drove down cost and improved performance. Cost alone was not enough, since some of the key technologies did not function adequately or could not be used widely enough – analog (1G) and digital (2G) networks, for example, could not run smartphones as data traffic was conducted over calls and transfer speeds were too slow. The introduction of GPRS technology (2.5G) solved these issues by allowing data to be sent all the time, increasing transfer rates dramatically. Meanwhile, after decades of development, touch screens worked well enough to use as 2007 approached. With sensors, processing power, and energy dense lithium-ion batteries also now in place, this was the last, albeit critical, piece of the jigsaw. Without any of these technologies reaching the threshold in cost and capability, the iPhone would not have been so disruptive. It was born through **technological convergence – the coming together of key technologies at a particular point in time to enable the creation of an entirely new product or service at a competitive cost.** It was, therefore, no coincidence that Apple introduced its first smartphone in 2007, the same year Google launched its Android operating system. In 2005, a $600 smartphone would not have been possible and by 2009, the ship had sailed.

> There's no chance that the iPhone is going to get any significant market share. No chance.
>
> Steve Ballmer, CEO of Microsoft, April 2007

Exponential S-Curve Adoption

Once the smartphone was launched in 2007, sales soared. By 2017, just ten years later, they topped a trillion dollars as the smartphone gained more than 80% market penetration. Adoption was non-linear and followed an S-curve – in all technology disruptions the pace appears slow at first because a new product has less than 1%-2% market penetration, then hits a tipping point and accelerates through an exponential phase until the product nears about 80% of the market, at which point growth slows as the market reaches saturation.

The iPhone's extraordinary success took most of the industry by surprise. Jim Balsillie, then co-CEO of Blackberry-maker RIM, predicted its impact on his business would be minimal, dismissing it as just "one more entrant into an already very busy space."[2]

Steve Ballmer, CEO of Microsoft at the time, was even more forthright: "There's no chance that the iPhone is going to get any significant market share. No chance."[3]

Figure 1. **Smartphone Share of Cellphone Market in U.S. 2007–2016 (%)**

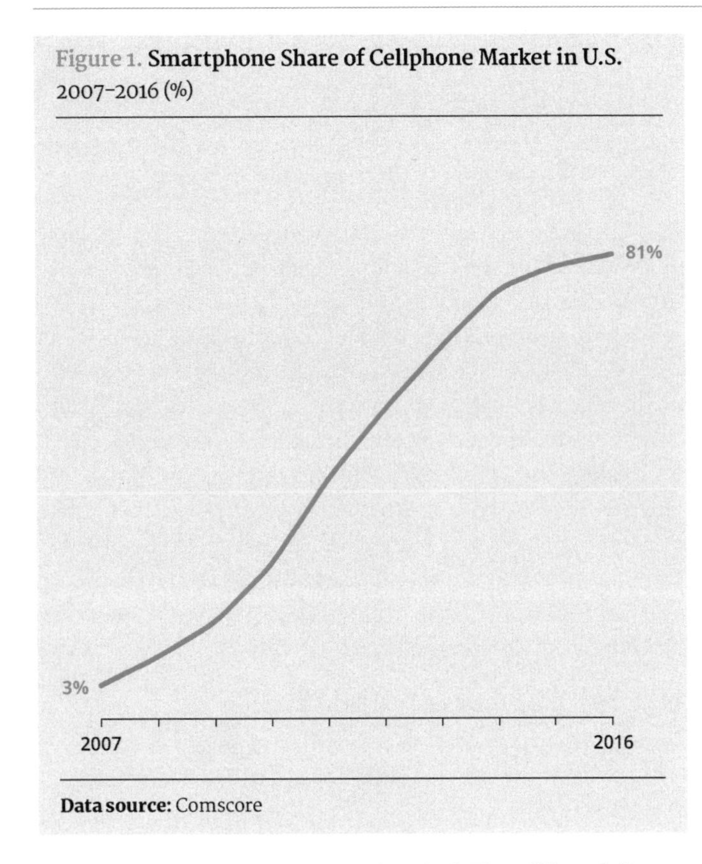

Data source: Comscore

Led by Outsiders

Neither Apple nor Google was a cellphone maker. In fact, neither company had any telecoms market expertise. The established giants of the industry such as Nokia, Blackberry, and Motorola were all blindsided by the emerging smartphone. This is usually the case – disruptors come from outside the core market. Think of the incumbent ice cutters, whalers, carriage, or camera makers, none of which led the disruption of their sectors. Hamstrung by protecting their existing product suite and locked into existing business models, thought processes, cultures, and incentive structures that favor incremental progress over disruptive innovation, incumbents find it difficult to develop and adapt quickly enough to entirely new product architectures, business models, or success metrics.

Many investors were also deeply skeptical. The trillion-dollar investment fund Capital Group, evoking the popular Harry Potter books of the time, said the iPhone's price meant it "lacks the ability to produce magical business growth… The old iPod magic doesn't translate here."[4] The media were also unconvinced, with PC Magazine, TechCrunch, and Bloomberg all publishing articles giving the iPhone little or no hope of success. MarketWatch even ran a comment piece advising Apple to "pull the plug on the iPhone" or "risk its reputation in competitive business".[5,6]

Cellphone disruptors like Nokia and Motorola were in a privileged position to drive the next wave of disruption, but they just did not see it happening so quickly. In a 2013 press conference, then Nokia CEO Stephen Elop said: "We didn't do anything wrong, but somehow we lost."[7]

Cascading Impact

Technology convergence opens up new possibilities and the smartphone created a period of extraordinary opportunity. At the start of 2007, Apple was valued at around $70bn. By 2020, the company was worth more than $1 trillion, making it one of the most valuable corporations in the world.[8] But the smartphone created huge possibilities far beyond the narrow confines of the cellphone market. The internet had gone mobile. This small, handheld device enabled not just the creation of new products and services, but also new business models that together disrupted sector after sector of the wider economy. Industries from music, banking, news, and restaurants to navigation, retail, education, and travel were transformed.

At the same time, the arrival of the smartphone triggered destruction of value on a shocking scale. The market share of Nokia, the leading phone maker at the time, slipped from 51% of the market in Q4 2007 to less than 3% just five years later as net sales slumped 75%.[9,10] The once ubiquitous brand has now all but disappeared. And just as the creation of value spread from sector to sector, so too did the destruction. Cameras were included in smartphones and as their quality improved, standalone cameras (both digital and what was left of the film market) became largely redundant. Despite an explosion in the number of photos taken, the formerly-dominant camera makers (both film and digital) and their value chains were effectively destroyed. The same can be said of MP3 players, GPS navigation devices, and handheld gaming consoles.

But the impact of the smartphone was felt far beyond the economy. Social lives were transformed as smartphones revolutionized how we communicated, made friends and contacts, and managed and expanded our personal and professional networks. The way we found jobs, worked, shopped, and entertained ourselves changed radically, almost overnight. The arrival of social media had an even greater transformative effect, completely upending traditional channels not just of communication but of information, as individuals could for the first time bypass traditional sources of news and analysis by creating their own content and sharing it with billions of people at the touch of a button. Dating was completely transformed – the percentage of heterosexual couples who met online went from 2% in 1995 to almost 40% in 2017.[11]

In the developing world, the smartphone had an even greater impact. The cellphone networks leapfrogged expensive (now obsolete) landline infrastructure, giving huge swathes of the population access to telephony and communications for the first time. Smartphones allowed people around the world to access banking and loans, business information, education, and entertainment in a way that was not previously possible. The lives of billions of people were instantly transformed.

All these new uses set in motion powerful forces (feedback loops) that fueled demand for smartphones, while each new user created more value for all existing users in a classic network effect. This helped drive demand, investment, and innovation ever higher while economies of scale pushed costs ever lower.

Unexpected Consequences

The explosion of the smartphone market also helped drive down the cost and increase the capabilities of all the underlying technologies, which then converged in different ways to disrupt other, apparently unrelated, sectors of the economy.

One example is ride-hailing, which only became possible thanks to the smartphone. Uber (founded in 2009), Ola (2010), Lyft (2012), and Didi (2012) have decimated the taxi markets in their respective countries, offering cheaper and more convenient rides. Often hamstrung by century-old regulatory models, licenses, or expensive medallions, established taxi operators have been unable to respond, other than by evolving into ride-hailing services themselves, such as Free Now. By 2016, just seven years after launching from an apartment in San Francisco, Uber had more bookings than the whole taxi industry in America.[12,13]

Figure 2. Cellphone and Landline Subscriptions
India 2001–2017 (per 100 People)

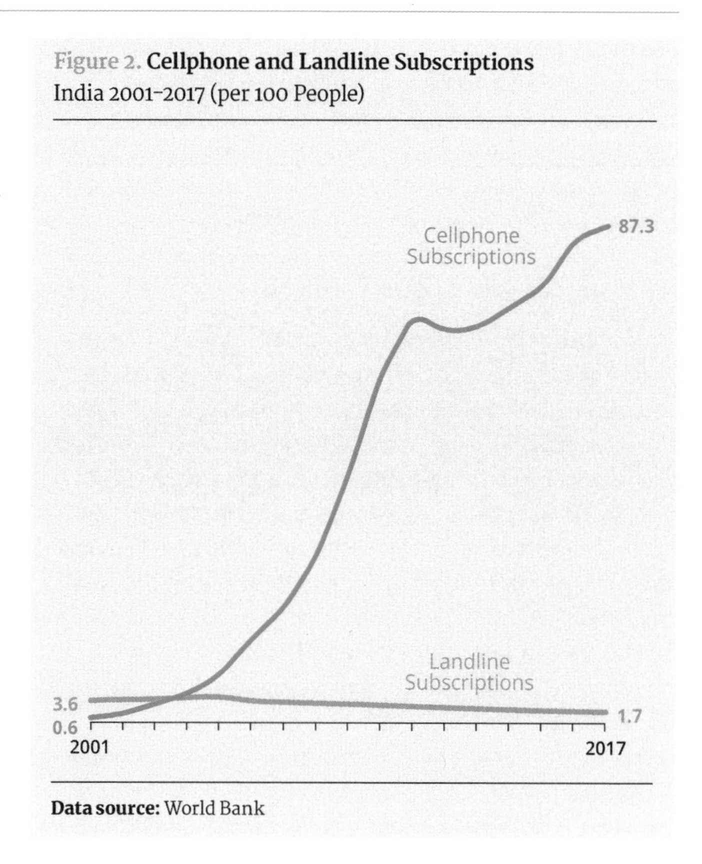

Data source: World Bank

But ride-hailing is just one dimension in the disruption of transportation. The improvement in lithium-ion battery costs, driven initially by the consumer electronics sector and then by the smartphone market, means electric vehicles (EVs) are now disrupting the high end of the gasoline vehicle market and are about to disrupt the mainstream market. The all-electric Tesla Model 3, for example, is now one of the best-selling cars in the US.[14]

At the same time, incredible strides are being made in developing autonomous vehicles (AVs). Again the cross-pollination is clear – Google, the company that created the first working AV and is helping lead the development of this market, is also the leader in global smartphone operating systems. Global ride-hailing companies such as Uber and Didi, both enabled by the smartphone disruption, have also invested billions of dollars to develop autonomous technology.

The convergence of ride-hailing, AVs, and EVs will soon create an entirely new form of transport known as Transportation-as-a-Service (TaaS) – essentially robo-taxis. This will be dramatically cheaper than car ownership, costing up to 10x less per mile and saving the average American family more than $5,600 a year (details are laid out in our *Rethinking Transportation 2020-2030* report), and trigger a rapid disruption of the gasoline car, bus, delivery van, and truck markets.

But the disruption of internal combustion engine (ICE) vehicles is not just about the dramatic cost reduction of autonomous electric vehicles (A-EVs) – the smartphone has also disrupted the value of individually-owned vehicles. In the past, the car was necessary for dating but now couples meet online. In the past, we needed the car to go to a restaurant or shop for food, but today a host of companies such as Amazon, Uber Eats, and GrubHub deliver fresh produce and ready-made meals to our front door. In the past, we needed a car to go and see a movie, but today streaming services like Netflix and Prime offer a monthly subscription to tens of thousands of movies and TV shows for less than the cost of a theater ticket. Information technology has unbundled and disrupted the value streams of the car, both practical and emotional, to the point where the individually-owned car is turning from an asset to a liability.

In a chain of complex causality, the smartphone has enabled the key technologies, products, and business model innovations that will kill off not just the ICE and individual car ownership, but the industry that fuels them – oil. The siloed, linear, mechanistic mindset points to the smartphone creating an 'App Economy' and disrupting telecoms, which is a true but narrow and dangerously incomplete assessment. In reality, the smartphone, the cloud, the internet, and AI are now converging to bring a swift end to two multi-trillion dollar, hundred-year-old industries together with a political, financial, and industrial order dominated by the geopolitics of oil.

Figure 3. **New York City Ride-Hailing Market**
2010-2019 (Rides/month)

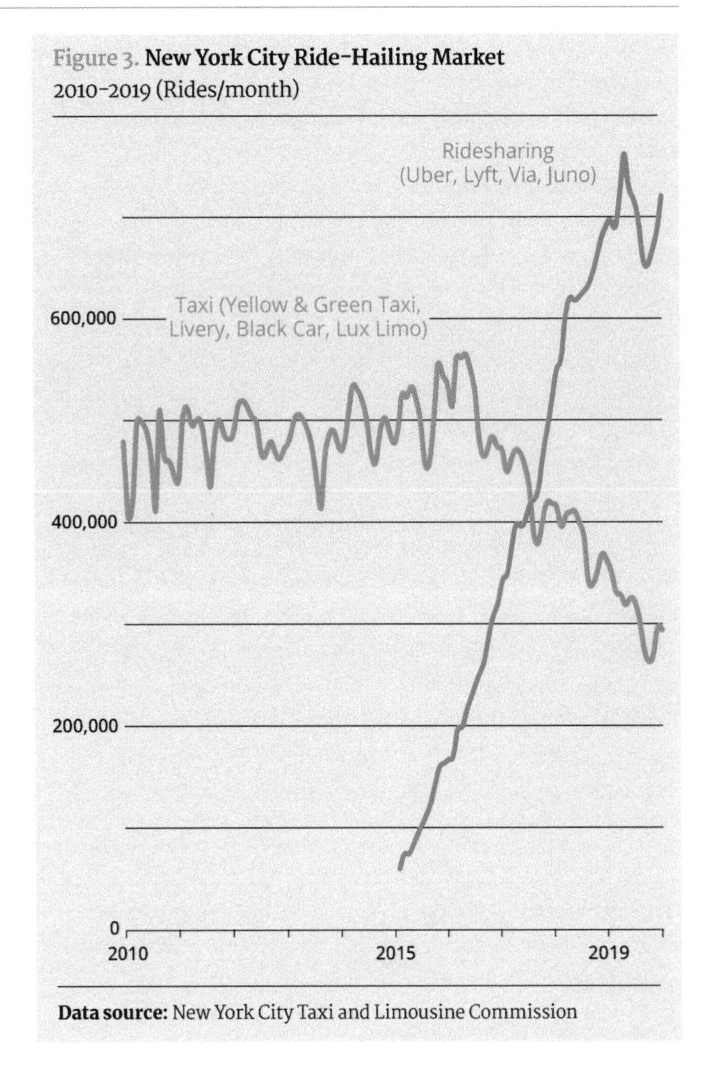

Data source: New York City Taxi and Limousine Commission

1.2 How the Car Transformed Society in the 20th Century

Technology Convergence

We have seen this pattern repeated throughout history, and nowhere more so than with the creation of the automobile. Innovations came thick and fast in the second half of the 19th century and the cost of key technologies fell dramatically. Steel rails produced with the Bessemer process cost $170 per ton in 1867, but by 1898 the cost had fallen to just $15 per ton.[15] The Otto combustion engine was developed in 1876 while the early discoveries of oil in the U.S. and developments in refining led to a plentiful supply of low-cost fuel. The vulcanization of rubber (1844) and the development of the pneumatic tire (1887) together replaced iron and wooden wheels that could not withstand the forces delivered by the ICE.

Photo: Kamloops substation with horse-drawn tank wagon, City of Vancouver Search Archives

All these technologies created the possibility of a new form of transportation, with the first gasoline cars appearing in Germany in 1887, closely followed by their U.S. counterparts in 1893. Early gasoline cars competed with electric and steam-powered alternatives and a decade passed before the cost and capabilities of the gasoline automobile reached the point where it became truly disruptive.

Key to this process was the assembly line. In 1890, a skilled butcher took eight to ten hours to slaughter and dress a steer on a farm. Chicago meatpacking factories did it in 35 minutes.[16] The innovation that made this possible was the moving disassembly line, where animals were slaughtered, butchered, processed, and packed before being shipped in railroad cars around the nation quickly and efficiently. Henry Ford rethought and flipped this model into a moving car assembly line, lowering manufacturing time and costs by an order of magnitude.

Figure 4. **Average Price of New Car in the U.S.** 1907–1916 ($)

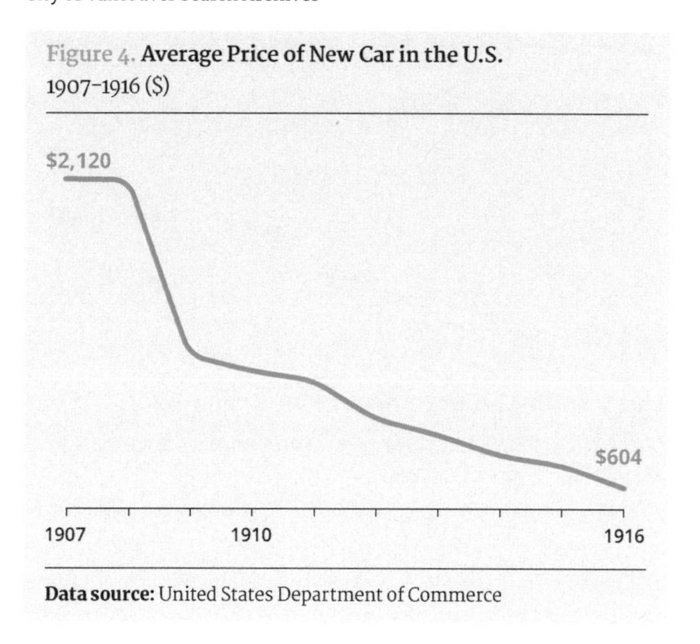

Data source: United States Department of Commerce

The Ford Model T, introduced in 1908, had a power-to-weight ratio 54 times higher than the 1885 Otto ICE[17] and cost $825 (about $41 per horsepower).[18] At the time, the price of a carriage and two (low end) horses was around $820 (about $410 per horsepower), meaning the Model T price/performance was 10x that of the leading mainstream mode of transportation.[19] The car was also superior in many other ways, including the speed it could travel, the amount of cargo it could carry, and the distance it could cover in a day.

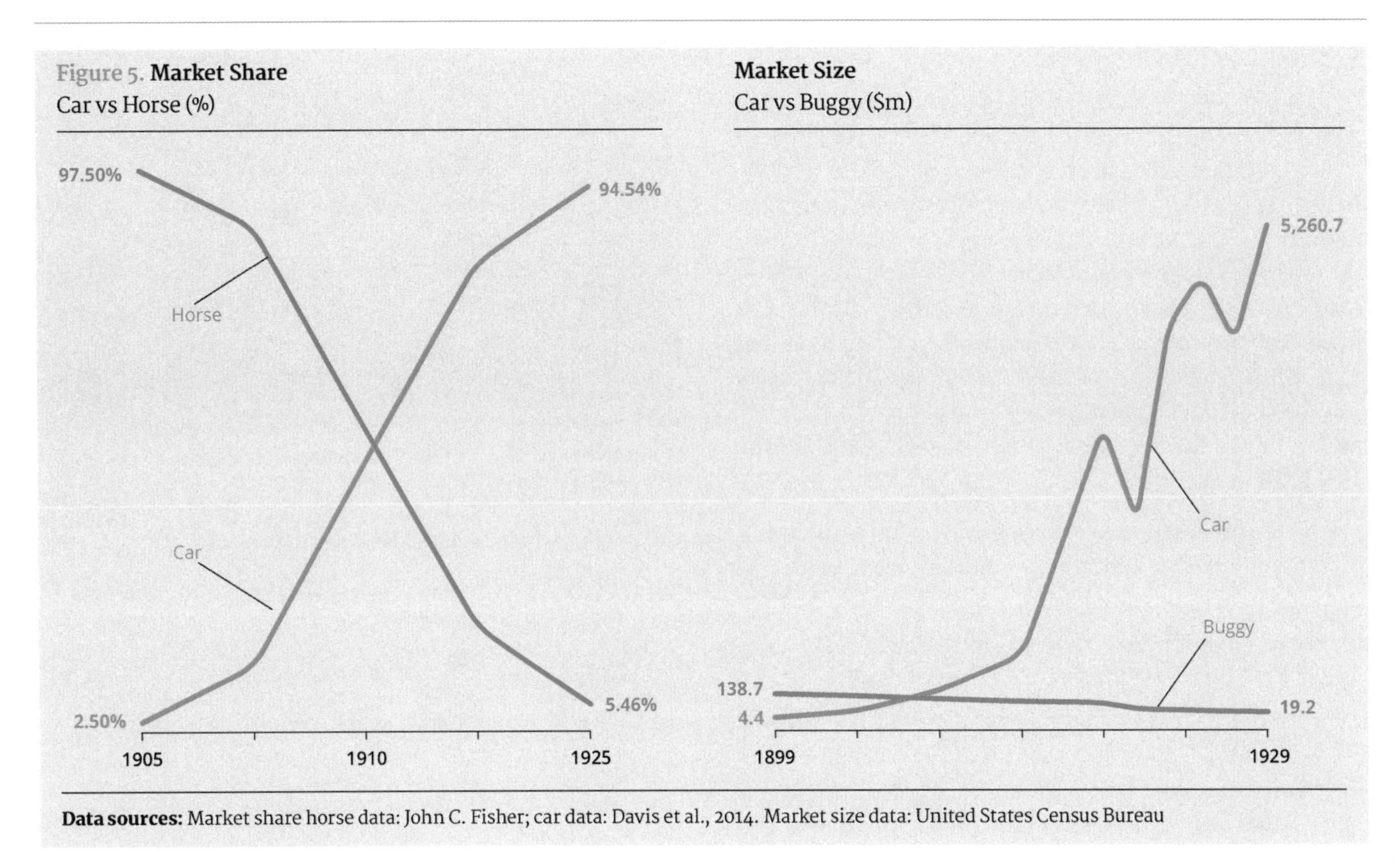

Data sources: Market share horse data: John C. Fisher; car data: Davis et al., 2014. Market size data: United States Census Bureau

Exponential S-Curve Adoption

Demand exploded. Car sales grew from a base of less than 5% of the vehicle fleet in 1905 to more than 95% in 1925. Adoption happened along an S-curve, with a 10-year phase between 1910 and 1920 taking market penetration from 11% to 81% – almost exactly the same time it took for the smartphone to dominate its market. But this growth was not just a replacement of carriage sales – the car created a whole new market for transport where none had existed previously (see Figure 5, right-hand graph).

The primary enablers of adoption were the relentless improvement in the car's capabilities and its rapidly-falling price. These were driven by increasing investment of capital and ingenuity and then, as demand increased, by economies of scale driving down the cost of production. Business model innovations such as auto finance made the automobile even easier to buy and expanded the market to the middle class, which eagerly embraced the car – by 1926, just seven years after its introduction, two thirds of cars were bought on credit.[20] In a virtuous cycle, increased market size attracted more investment, more talent, and more competitors, which brought yet more innovation to drive costs down further and made cars more affordable to more people, leading to increased sales.

As demand grew, the market responded and adapted in predictable ways – entrepreneurs, suppliers, and even the government rushed to take advantage of the new opportunities and investment dollars flooded in. Infrastructure was built up around these new industries – road building exploded, the oil industry took off, and gas stations (the first of which was built in 1905) were rolled out, numbering 15,000 by 1920 and 124,000 by 1930.[21]

The car industry actually built the machinery that built its own infrastructure in a recursive, virtuous cycle as combustion engines powered earthwork (excavators, loaders, dozers, graders, and scrapers), roadwork (milling machines, pavers, and compactors), and lifting machinery (tower cranes and tractor cranes), further accelerating change.[22]

Policy Innovation was also adopted along S-curves. The gasoline tax was first introduced in Oregon in February 1919 and within just six years, 91% of U.S. states had adopted it. Within 10 years, every state in the Union taxed gas (see Figure 6).[23]

This rapid adoption happened in spite of what, in 1900, seemed like insurmountable barriers to the automobile. In fact at this time, the ICE was competing with other technologies such as steam and electric power. Not only were gasoline cars expensive and unreliable, but there were almost no paved roads in the U.S., the oil industry was in its infancy, and there were no gas stations (mobile horse-powered fuel wagons brought gasoline and kerosene to early cars). Nor was there any real manufacturing capacity or supply chains. The rules of the road had not yet been developed and almost no-one knew how to drive, a deadly combination that led to numerous accidents and, subsequently, calls for restrictions and even bans on the use of this 'lethal' new invention.

A swift and dramatic shift in public opinion was another crucial factor. In 1900, people were broadly skeptical of automobiles, viewing them as expensive, unreliable, and dangerous. Horses and carriages, on the other hand, were known quantities, trusted, and even loved. Few could imagine a world without them. But as cars became ever-more visible and reliable, skepticism turned to fascination and then desire. Conversely, the trusted horse came to be seen as increasingly outdated, dirty, and obsolete. This change in public perception acted as a powerful accelerator of change and happened despite an active resistance campaign from incumbents.

All these barriers turned out to be variables, not constants – they fell away remarkably quickly as the drivers of supply, demand, and regulation no longer acted as brakes on adoption, but as accelerators. What had appeared as roadblocks turned out to be little more than speed bumps. We see echoes of these 'barriers' in the EV and TaaS narrative today.

Cascading Impact

Just like the smartphone, the impact of the automobile was felt right across the economy. This was not just a one-to-one technology substitution but a fundamentally different transportation system that opened up extraordinary possibilities. The economic benefits were almost immeasurable – in some ways, the U.S. economy was built around the automobile, its ancillary industries, and the impact it had on wider society.

By the 1930s, one in every seven Americans was in employment linked to the auto industry – for example the number of garage laborers grew by 600% between 1910 and 1920.[28] Whole new industries in auto insurance and finance appeared. The car ushered in the shopping mall and changed the very structure of the retail industry. The impact on raw materials was equally profound as steel, oil, and rubber replaced iron, animal feed, and wood. In just 10 years, the auto industry went from a minor buyer to becoming the leading consumer of steel, with demand skyrocketing from 70,000 tons in 1910 to one million tons by 1920.[29] Increased investment in the steel industry as a result pushed costs down further and brought innovations like corrosion-free stainless steel, which opened new possibilities in applications from surgical implants, food and beverage equipment, and construction.

Experts Fail to See It

"Americans are a horse loving-nation... the widespread adoption of the motor-driven vehicle in this country is open to serious doubt."
Lippincott's magazine, 1903.[24]

"I do not believe the introduction of motor cars will ever affect the riding of horses."
Mr Scott-Montague, United Kingdom MP, 1903.[25]

"Humankind has traveled for centuries in conveyances pulled by beasts, why would any reasonable person assume the future holds anything different?"
Carriage Monthly, 1904.[26]

Even in 1912, the car was perceived as a threat only to the top end of the buggy market: **"Though the shift understandably distressed the affected firms, observers took comfort that the high-grade horse drawn vehicles accounted for a relatively small percentage of the trade; losses here hardly imperiled the entire industry."**
Carriage Association of America.[27]

Figure 6. **U.S. States Imposing Gasoline Tax**
(%)

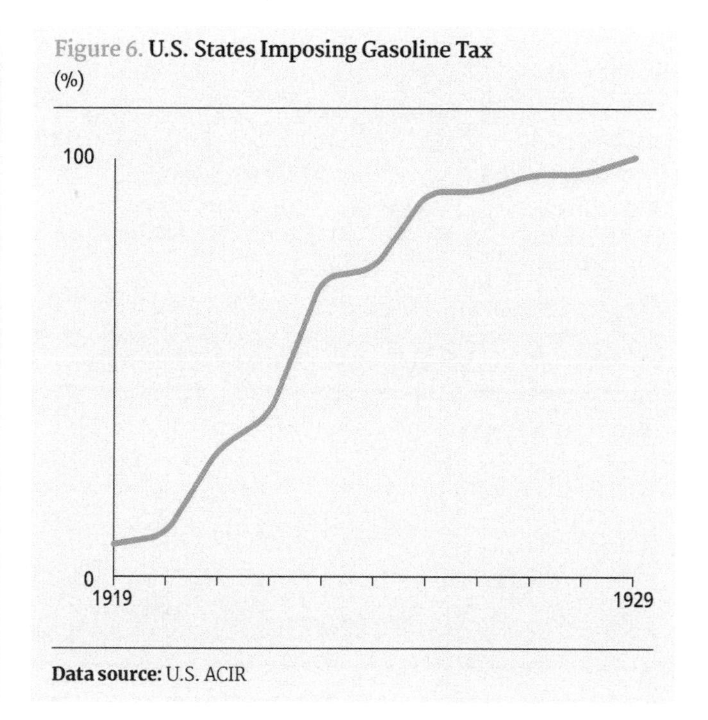

Data source: U.S. ACIR

Framework Box 2. Systems Dynamics: Feedback Loops

Brakes

Supply, demand, and regulation provide powerful brakes on the adoption of new products and services. The incumbent system is protected by sunk costs in building infrastructure, benefits from large economies of scale and investment, and is supported by legislative frameworks and policy that have often been designed around it. Public opinion is supportive as consumers are accustomed and often attached to a product or service and are skeptical of alternatives. Value chains are mature. These all help lock the system in place.

The prospect of change can trigger resistance from incumbent businesses, workers, unions, governments, and consumers. Businesses typically follow an incumbents' 'playbook' that includes lobbying to create regulatory barriers to protect markets and creating doubt about new products or services through pseudo-science or scaremongering, which can include buying and killing disruptors.

In the early stages of disruption, these brakes can create powerful resistance to change. However, as costs and capabilities improve, new products and services become increasingly disruptive. The brakes begin to weaken.

Accelerators

As new products and services are adopted, powerful systems dynamics are unleashed that can accelerate the process of disruption. These accelerators drive demand (cost and capabilities, and public opinion), supply (production, investment, and infrastructure) and regulation (policy and tax) for new products and services, but can also drive destruction of the existing industry.

Accelerators also include network effects, where increased demand increases value for the network, driving further demand, and rebound effects, where falling costs lead to increasing demand. They also include recursion, where technologies are used to develop the infrastructure that supports them.

They can trigger non-linear effects including exponential improvements in cost and capability and S-curve adoption for new products and services, and death spirals for the old. These accelerators can be seen as the primary (first order) drivers of adoption.

Ripple Effects

Disruptions seldom remain confined to a single industry or sector. Instead, their effects ripple out and profoundly impact many other parts of the system, including the individual sector (the supply, manufacturing and distribution chains, and infrastructure), other sectors, and social, economic, political, and biophysical systems. These impacts can then ripple back to affect disruption in the original sector. These ripple effects can be seen as the secondary (second order) drivers of disruption.

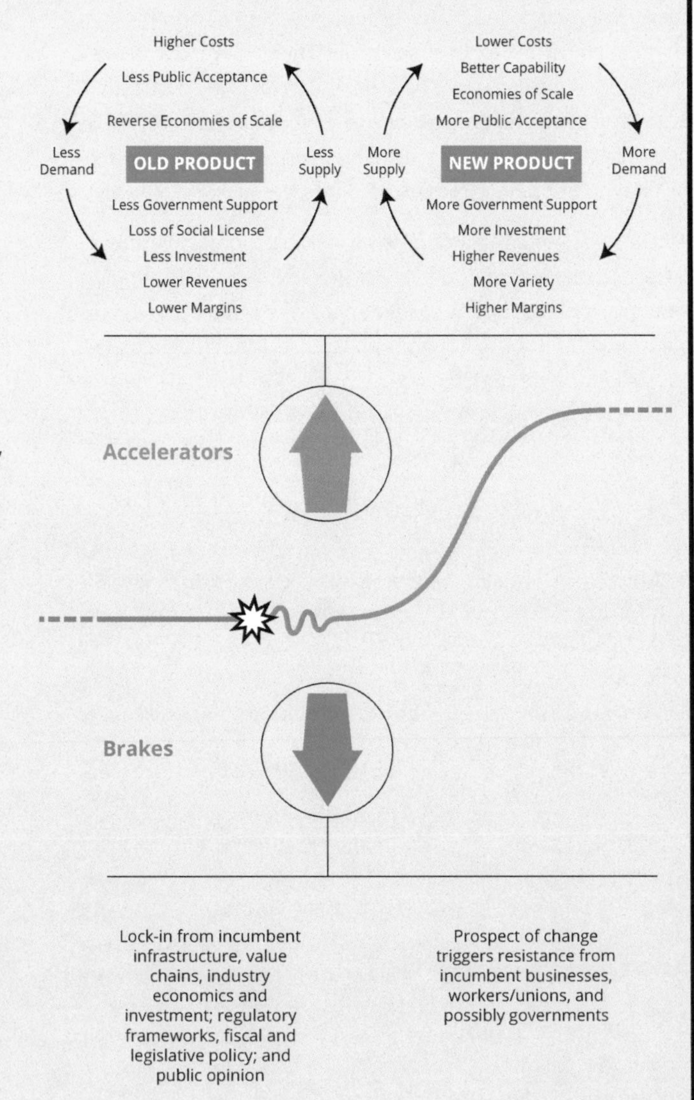

Source: RethinkX

The car industry also played a more direct role in the growth of the U.S. middle class by raising incomes. In 1914, Ford doubled its workers' wages, raising eyebrows throughout the industry and beyond. Two years later, profits had doubled and within seven years it owned half the U.S. auto market. The move to attract and retain talent had proved a masterstroke. "The payment of $5 a day for an eight-hour day was one of the finest cost-cutting moves we ever made," Henry Ford later said.[30] Soon industry throughout the country found itself emulating Ford.

But alongside this extraordinary economic growth there was also destruction of value. The carriage industry was all but wiped out – of the 13,000 carriage makers operating in the U.S. in 1890, only a handful were in business by 1920.[31] Those industries servicing horse and carriages were hit equally hard – between 1910 and 1920, the number of stable hands in the U.S. dropped by 70%.[32] Existing value chains were also hit hard – in 1915, 22% of U.S. cropland (about 93 million acres) as well as 80 million acres of pastureland was used to feed horses and mules. By 1960, all but five million acres had been freed for other uses – mostly for beef and dairy cows.[33]

Unexpected Consequences

But the car's impact was not limited to the economy. Its introduction led to huge changes in the built environment as houses, towns, and cities were redesigned around this radical new form of transport. It changed where we lived and worked, and where we built our schools, shops, hospitals, and factories. For the first time, people moved out of towns into the suburbs in huge swathes and needed cars to commute to and from work.[34,35] Meanwhile, drive-in diners, movie theaters, malls, and big-box stores all became part of the urban landscape.

The car also played an important role in our culture, helping drive the first phase of the sexual revolution as young people found new ways of escaping parental control, while giving people of all ages far more independence and opportunity. Indeed the driving test became a cultural rite of passage for teenagers – a new marker of the transition from childhood to adulthood. Motor tourism opened up the whole country to the newly-mobile American population as 'road trip' and the 'open road' entered the national lexicon. Autocamping became a popular activity.[36] National Parks and the automobile, both relatively new ideas, enabled each other's growth, popularity, and cultural hold on America's imagination.

America's car companies even made a huge contribution to the country's 20th century military domination. During World War II, Ford shifted production at 42 domestic plants to produce war goods as well as military hardware for other Allied nations.[37,38] Indeed the car helped transform international relations as the rise of the U.S. as a global superpower was supported and amplified by its dominance of the oil and auto industries. The productivity benefits that came with this new transport industry were felt across all sectors, cementing U.S. leadership in other markets and driving the levels of immigration and investment through the 20th century that helped accelerate U.S. growth and innovation further.

The car had impacted every aspect of society and, in doing so, had gone from a 'nice to have' to a necessity. To participate fully in life, both economically and socially, required access to this new form of transport. And as the economy, culture, built environment, and governance structures coevolved with the auto industry, it became ever more locked-in. After the explosive adoption in the early years, the past hundred years have seen a long period of incremental improvement to the product within a value chain, business model, and market structure that have remained largely unchanged.

Photo: Ford Motor Co., Highland Park, 1913

Framework Box 3. Change at Sector Level

There is a fractal quality to patterns of change in human systems. The same pattern of long periods of incremental change interspersed with rapid disruption is seen in every sector of the economy. Technological capabilities in the sector can improve or its geographical reach can expand, but the structure of the system in terms of the value chain (production, supply, and distribution), infrastructure, and regulation remain broadly constant. The structure of the transport and energy systems, for example, has remained broadly the same over the past 100 years. Occasionally, however, a convergence of factors triggers a phase change.

- An incumbent system is kept stable by constraining factors that act to resist change. These brakes can weaken over time.
- Technologies improve in cost and capabilities and converge to enable a disruptive new product or service to outcompete an existing one.
- Disruption happens quickly, despite perceived barriers including strong resistance to change and a deeply-embedded system. These barriers are not constants, but variables.
- Adoption is non-linear and follows an S-curve. It is driven by accelerating feedbacks that affect the cost and capabilities of products, demand, supply, and regulation.
- Economic destruction of the existing industry happens early, before the new disruptive industry reaches maturity, and the impact is often disproportionate to the scale of change. Leverage (both financial and operating) means that a small downturn in demand can bankrupt an industry. This market trauma is like a forest fire – just a small change in the system is needed to bring about quick and brutal destruction of the old, while the new may take years to emerge.
- Disruptors tend to come from outside the incumbent industry. Incumbent mindsets, incentives, practices, and business models blind existing businesses to the new reality. They double down on the old model rather than create the new.
- A linear, mechanistic, siloed mindset prevents us from seeing the speed and extent of disruptions in advance.
- Disruptions represent phase changes – they are not just the like-for-like substitution of technologies (where "all else remains equal"). They enable new business models, metrics, and incentives. The new system can be fundamentally different to the old in terms of the structure of the value chain, how value is delivered (business model), the metrics and incentives that drive consumers (demand), producers and investors (supply), and policymakers (regulation).
- Disruptions open up possibilities across the value chain, connected sectors, the wider economy, and society. Disruptions of foundational sectors have profound impacts that ripple across not just the economy but the whole of society. These impacts can act as feedback loops impacting the cost and capabilities of technologies and other aspects of the system, acting as secondary drivers of disruption.

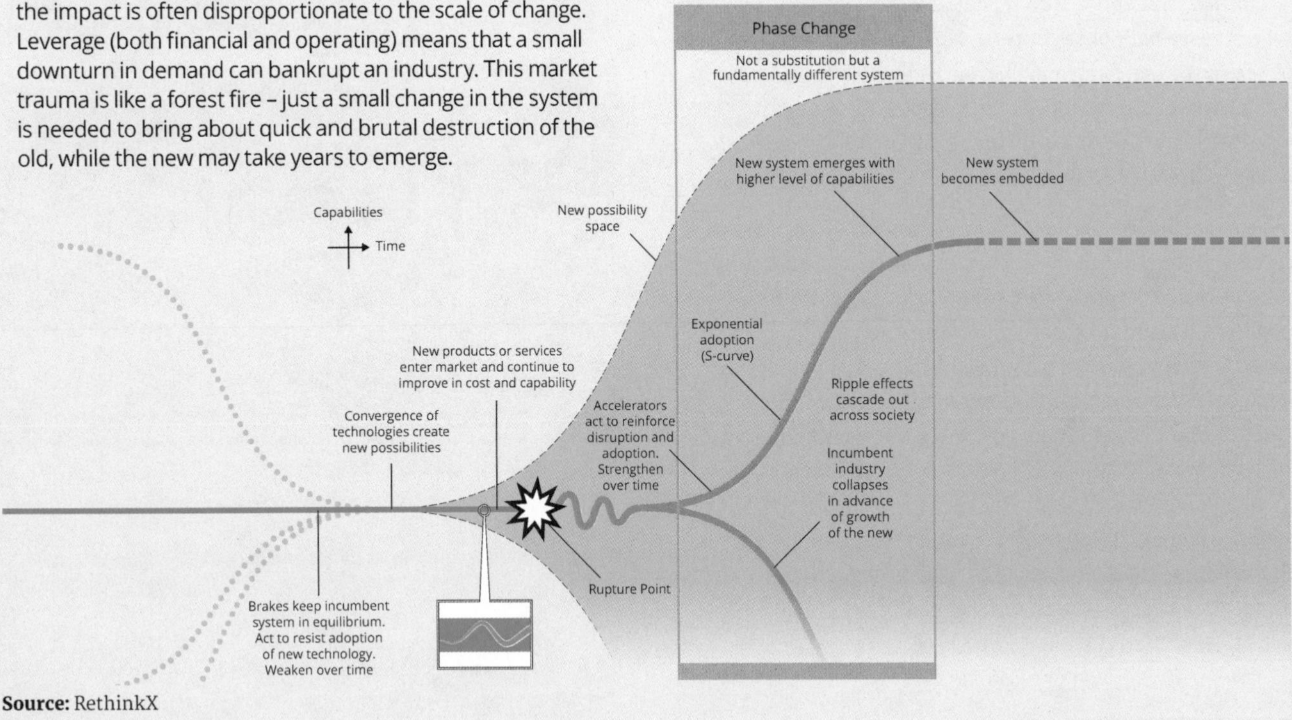

Source: RethinkX

Framework Box 4. Failure of Forecasting: The Linear Mindset

Almost all analyses from government, NGOs, banks, consultants, and other prognosticators are linear in three dimensions:

1. Linear Trends. Extrapolating past and present conditions and trends as a heuristic to predict the future.
2. Linear Causality. Treating the system as simple and mechanistic – A causes B and "all else remains equal" (only accounting for first order effects of change).
3. Sector silos. Treating each sector of the economy as its own independent system, whereas in fact everything is interrelated.

Any sector of the economy, and indeed society as a whole, is a complex system. Change in complex systems is non-linear, driven by the interaction of feedback loops and systems dynamics (see Framework Box 3). This non-linearity is seen, for example, in the S-curve adoption of new technologies.

The linear approach is a reasonable approximation of the future during periods of incremental progress (point A), when self-correcting feedbacks (brakes) dominate and constrain change, but it is woefully inadequate as disruption approaches (point B) and self-reinforcing feedbacks (accelerators) take over.

This has many consequences, including a failure to anticipate both the speed of change and the impact of change on an individual system and those connected to it, and a failure to appreciate the expanded range of possibilities as the system moves out of equilibrium.

At a sector level, this leads analysts to assume the barriers to adoption will continue indefinitely – essentially assuming they are constants when they are variables. They change, and they change fast, just as we have seen with the high cost of automobiles, their unreliability, and the lack of infrastructure supporting them. At the broader level, this failure leads to a narrow and siloed viewpoint that ignores the broader effects on society.

As we enter the most disruptive decade in human history, with every sector of the economy on the cusp of disruption, this failure matters. Whether we are planning investments, education, social and environmental policy, or infrastructure spending, narrow linear mindsets blind us to the emerging possibilities and the pace and scale of change approaching – society is hurtling towards the future with a blindfold on.[39]

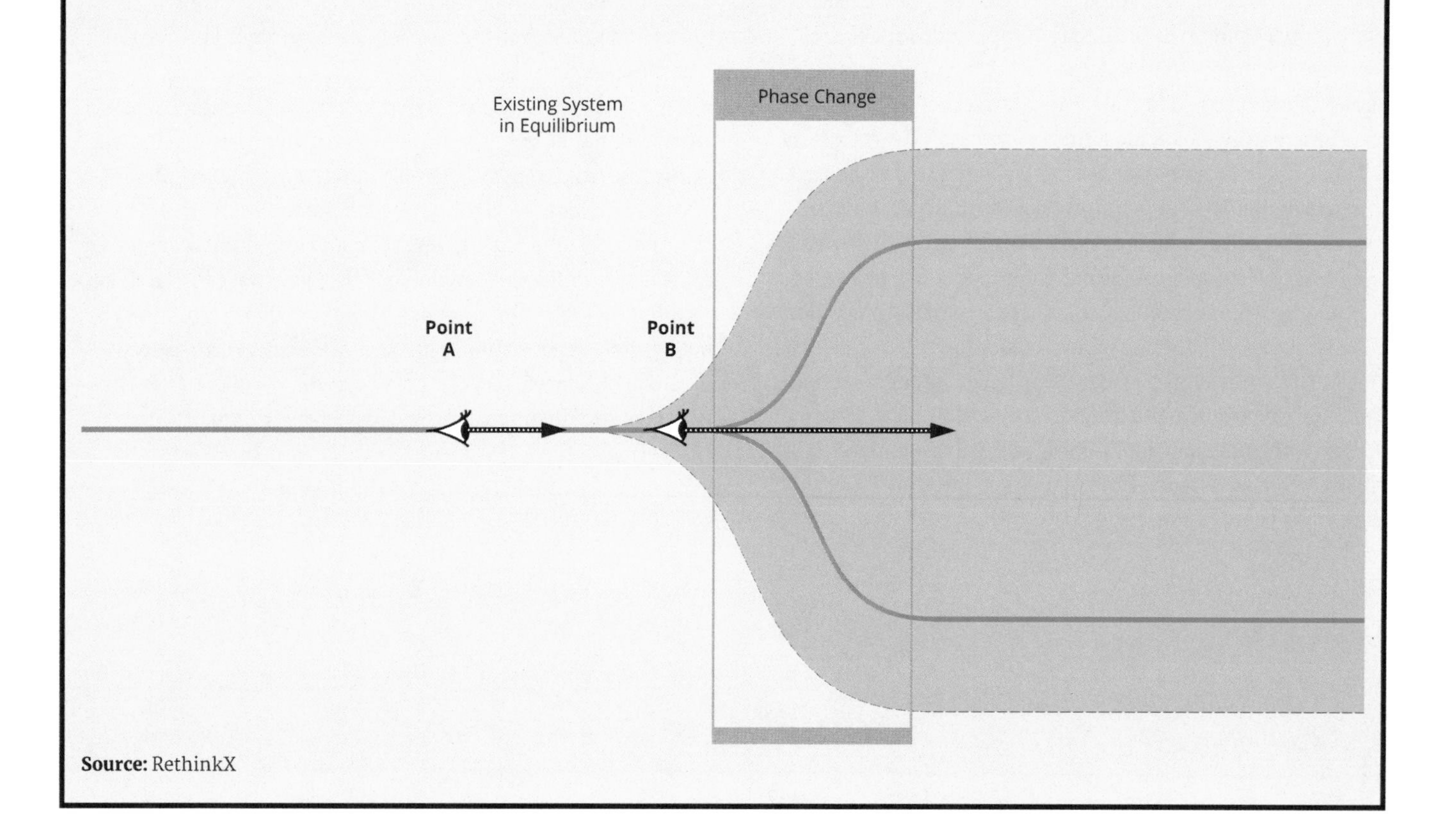

Source: RethinkX

1.3 How the Printed Book Enabled Europe's Breakthrough

The same pattern can be seen with the introduction of a new technology product in Europe in the 15th century, but with even more profound consequences.

The printed book triggered cascading waves of disruption that lasted centuries and impacted every aspect of society, fundamentally changing our view of the world and our place within it. It was the first wave of technological progress that enabled the Industrial Revolution, which led to an entirely new system of production as well as new social, economic, and political systems to organize and manage society. More than that, it created extraordinary new possibilities for humanity that required new ways of understanding and explaining the world.

In a web of complex causality, the printed book was both the cause and effect of fundamental changes to society that were already underway by the 15th century. For almost a thousand years, the Dark Ages cast a long shadow over Europe as ignorance, dogma, and poverty triumphed over knowledge, rationality, and progress. But out of this seemingly hopeless desolation, rays of light began to emerge.

Trade slowly began to flourish as trade routes were gradually reopened and ideas developed and spread as the city states of southern Europe began to prosper once more. The increasing availability of capital in the hands of the merchant class and the developing universities helped nurture a new thirst for knowledge and innovation. The Mediterranean region again became a melting pot of ideas and concepts developed locally, rediscovered from earlier times, and imported from the East (where a higher level of technological capability and social complexity had been maintained).[40] Attracted by the increasing openness to ideas and people of Renaissance Italy, by 1500 around 5,000 Greek intellectuals had migrated to Venice alone.[41] They brought with them secular scholarship, knowledge, and ideas that defined Europe's new identity and brought lasting change.[42] The result was a dramatic rise in the number of manuscripts published in Europe starting in the 12th century, creating further demand for information and knowledge that the monks could scarcely keep pace with.

Figure 7. **Number of Manuscripts Produced in Western Europe**
6th–15th Century

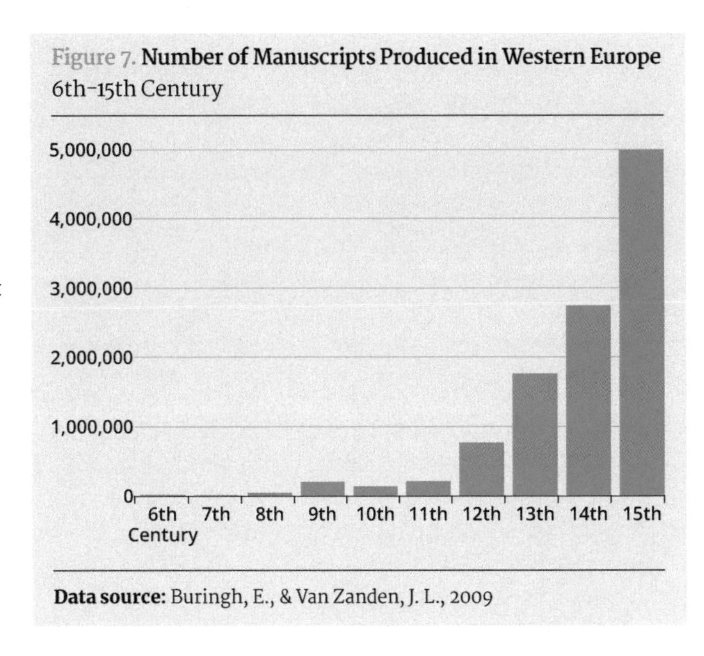

Data source: Buringh, E., & Van Zanden, J. L., 2009

This context is key, for it was no coincidence that the printed book had such an impact in Europe, whereas its influence in China and Korea centuries earlier had been limited.[43] Not only had these societies not fallen into a dark age and therefore not seen an explosion in demand for books, but their complex writing systems, with thousands instead of dozens of characters, meant the printed book offered no real economic or time advantage over manuscripts. Furthermore, Europe had hundreds of states (cities, republics, and kingdoms) competing for trade, technologies, and people in a way that China did not.[44] New technologies alone are not, therefore, deterministic – they need the right governing structures and societal conditions in which to flourish. For the printed book, Europe, rather than the then-dominant East, provided this environment.

Technology Convergence

Again, a convergence of technologies was the catalyst. Parchment, made from sheep, goat, cow, and other animal skins, was the main technology used by European scribes throughout the Middle Ages. But parchment was expensive – more than 200 sheep were required to make one Bible.[45] A new technology in the form of paper was brought to Europe in the 12th century from China by Islamic traders and by the 15th century it had largely replaced parchment in manuscript production. The first key enabling technology was now in place, but advances in ink technology, metallurgy, and machining, leading to the invention of metal, movable typeface, were necessary to make the printing press possible. Again, the cross-pollination of technologies across different sectors was key – the first printing press was a modified wine press traditionally used to press grapes and olives. All these technologies came together in the 1450s with the invention of the Gutenberg Printing Press.

The impact was immediate and profound – a page could now be printed in just a few minutes, 200 times faster than hand-written manuscripts (not including the time to typeset the book).[46] The first paper Bibles that came out of Gutenberg's workshop in around 1454 cost 30 Florins – 10x less than a manuscript Bible.[47] Competition, technology improvements, and scale pushed book prices down even further. By 1483, the cost of printing had fallen so far that the Ripoli press in Florence charged three Florins for 1,025 copies of Plato's Dialogues, whereas a scribe would charge one Florin for a single copy.[48]

Exponential S-Curve Adoption

The printing press itself quickly spread throughout Europe, due in part to the religious violence that plagued medieval Europe. Just a few years after Gutenberg printed the first Bible in Mainz, the city was sacked.[49] Its skilled cadre of printers packed up and left predominantly for Italian cities such as Rome, Verona, Naples, Florence, and Venice, with universities that were hungry to publish and consume knowledge,[50] but also for Lyon, Paris, and Valencia.[51] Book production rose exponentially, from five million copies in the 15th century to one billion by the 18th century, as prices continued to drop as technology and production processes improved. For the first time, individuals could afford to buy books. This led to dramatic increases in literacy that boosted book sales and enabled new thoughts and ideas to circulate quickly and widely, with huge implications for society.

Cascading Impact and Unexpected Consequences

The book invited personal reflection and abstract thinking that helped give rise to individualism – initially in Northwest Europe on the edge of the economic powers of the time, Venice and Genoa.[52] Centuries of received wisdom were soon overturned. The church and state began to lose control over access to information. The ideas of reformers such as John Wycliff and Martin Luther could now be disseminated far more freely among the wider population, helping the Reformation gain momentum across Europe. The printing press was also instrumental in the spread of ideas of the early humanists such as Petrarch and Renaissance philosophers such as Pico della Mirandola, which in turn laid the foundations for the Enlightenment and Scientific Revolution. This information revolution enabled and then fed into ongoing developments in science, technology, philosophy, and the arts and enabled an acceleration in the development and diffusion of ideas. Francis Bacon, Isaac Newton, John Locke, Galileo, Descartes, Darwin, and others found new ways to understand and explain the physical world and develop the scientific method that underpinned the new mechanized system of production that emerged through the Industrial Revolution. Along with this extraordinary technological progress, new ways of organizing and managing society (a new Organizing System) emerged as the medieval social, political, and economic systems were undermined and outcompeted by societies better adapted to the emerging possibilities.

Empiricism and the scientific method replaced religion as a more effective way of explaining the world. City states coalesced into nation states as the emerging production system required greater scale and reach to compete. Monarchy was replaced by democracy and the church separated from the state. Free-market capitalism overturned feudal systems and the barter economy and individuals became empowered to receive the rewards of their own effort (a new social contract). The printed book was, therefore, the first wave of technological progress that helped Europe massively increase its societal capabilities beyond those of any previous civilization.

The Organizing System

The Organizing System encompasses the prevailing models of thought, belief systems, myths, values, abstractions, and conceptual frameworks that help explain how the world works. It comprises the political, social, and economic systems, including the governing structures, institutions, and culture, that oversee, influence, and manage society and provide the incentives (compulsion and reward) that drive the decisions, actions, and beliefs of individuals and groups.

In the Western system, this manifests in concepts such as the primacy of empiricism, secular scholarship and the scientific method, individual rights, political democracy, nation states, free-market capitalism, and a social contract where we trade our labor for capital and expect some sort of safety net in return. These are a series of interrelated modules and the development of each influences the effectiveness and evolution of the others.

Successful Organizing Systems enable increases in societal capabilities. That is, they help societies capture the possibilities opened up by technology and create the conditions for further technological progress. They make higher-level, more complex civilizations possible by creating the social stability required through the 'push' (laws, regulation, power) and the 'pull' (incentives, desire, awe) that, in turn, lead to further innovation, competitive advantage, military capabilities, prosperity, and power.

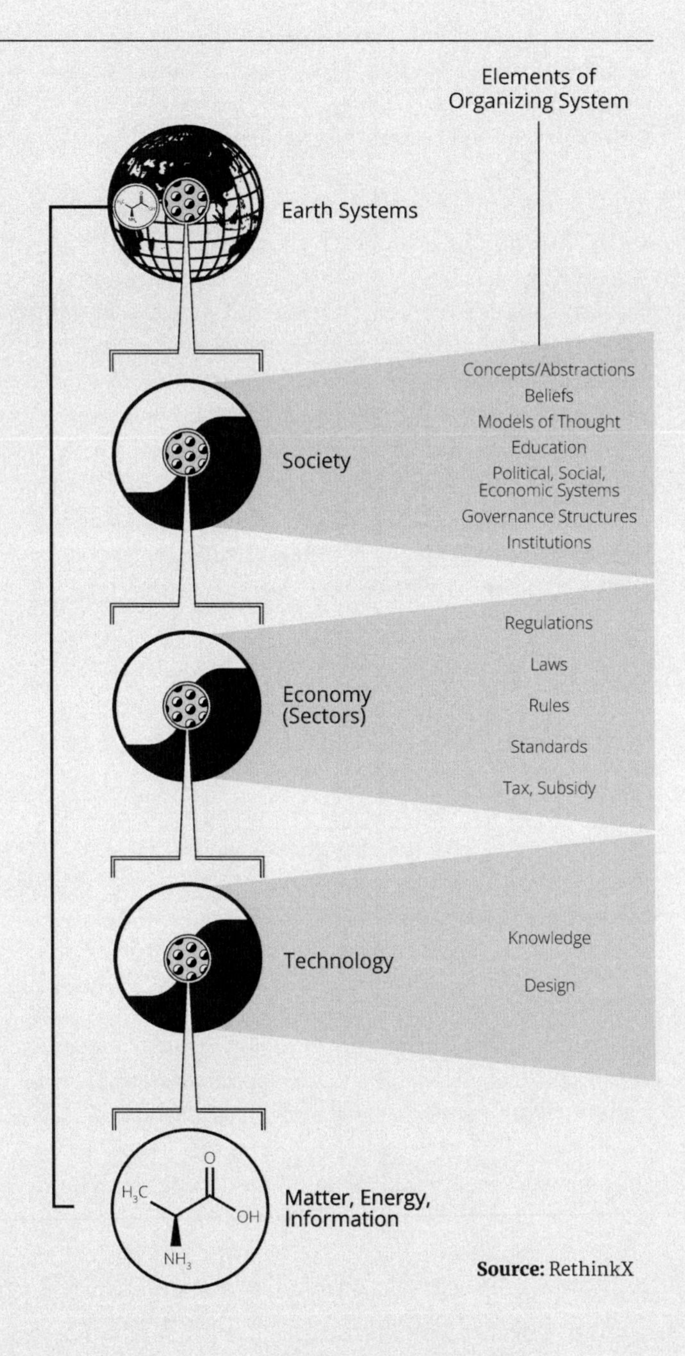

Source: RethinkX

Coevolution of Technology and Organizing Systems

As civilizations have evolved ever-greater technological capabilities, and with them the ability to operate at greater scale, reach, and complexity, they have needed to evolve ever-greater organizational capabilities in tandem. The Organizing System thus coevolves with the technologies of the day (which together make up the system of production) – it creates the conditions that enable technological progress and its own evolution is affected by the technologies that develop under its guidance.

Organizing Systems evolve in ways that resemble biological organisms – those best suited to the economic, technological, and geographical conditions in a given era or place thrive and are replicated. Copy, paste, and adapt, either through mimicry or conquest. The various components that make up the Organizing System should not be thought of as mechanical parts, but as subsystems that interact and overlap with each other. There is no 'right' combination in any era or society and the evolution of each aspect and the combinations that develop are not planned or designed, but emerge (self-organize) over time through experimentation (trial and often painful error) and competition.

Geography has also played a vitally important role in determining the success of leading civilizations in terms of the availability of key resources, not least soil fertility, sources of freshwater, energy, materials, and transport routes for trade and military capability. The importance of geography changes over time and is dependent on the technological capabilities of an era – an early civilization might be dependent on the fertility of the soil and availability of natural resources immediately surrounding it, while a civilization with more advanced transportation and energy technologies can free itself from these constraints and access fertile soil and materials further afield. For example, Rome – a backwater in the Mediterranean empires of Egypt, Phoenicia, and Babylonia, far removed from the productive lands of the Fertile Crescent – found itself ideally placed at the center of the Mediterranean basin as large rowing and sailing boats, and road and bridge building, were developed, giving access to a far greater area to extract from, control, and influence.

Thus, technological progress alone does not determine the capabilities or relative competitiveness of any society – the Organizing System and geography have also been critically important. The best combination that is available dictates the winners – for example a civilization of 10,000 people requires very different systems than one of 100,000, which requires a different system than one of one million people.

While the technological capabilities dictate the potential (the 'capability frontier') of any civilization, the Organizing System determines how close to this potential a society can get (in terms of its societal capabilities). This depends on how well the Organizing System can compel or encourage productivity and technological innovation, enable optimal decisions to be taken across society, and manage, control, govern, and influence its population. This effect is apparent today, for despite global availability of technologies, the societal capabilities of the U.S. have not been matched in many parts of the world due to less adaptive Organizing Systems. Even within a country there may be variations. For example, the Organizing System of an area such as Silicon Valley has been far more effective at improving technological capabilities than much of the rest of the U.S., just like New York had the Organizing System that outcompeted the rest of the country in the 19th century.

Organizing Systems have the capacity to adapt to changing conditions – essentially broadening the range of conditions in which they can function and thrive – but their adaptive capacity is limited in speed and scale.[53] Historically, fundamental change in societal capabilities has happened only when civilizations collapse or as new civilizations break through, when a new Organizing System emerges to replace one that can no longer adapt fast enough to order-of-magnitude improvements in technological capabilities.

Organizing Systems are human constructs, but their elements can appear, in any given time and place, incontrovertible and unchangeable. Few in the U.S. today would question the concept of the nation state, representative democracy, or individual rights as once the belief in the divine right of kings, geocentrism, or the philosopher's stone went unchallenged. However, over the history of civilization, elements of Organizing Systems have changed dramatically – what was once seen as a fundamental truth becomes little more than a footnote in history.

Part 2

Rethinking the Past: The History of Humanity

2.1 Humanity 1.0: The Age of Survival

If we look back through human history, we can see two fundamentally distinct ages with very different determinants of success.

For millennia, humans saw little improvement in quality of life, eking out an existence by fishing, hunting, and gathering plants and animals. The fundamental driver of this age was survival. Technological change was extremely slow moving and confined to portable tools and strategies that helped in the battle for survival. The limitations of muscle transportation, word-of-mouth communications, and human memory restricted the ability to develop and disseminate technological improvements through time and space.

Humans were organized in small groups limited to dozens or hundreds of individuals. These communities, egalitarian by necessity, had little use for belongings that served any purpose other than survival. With no means of storing food, most of their time was spent planning, finding, and gathering food, energy, and materials.

Humans consumed nature's bounty, which meant they had to live according to nature's seasonal and climatic flows. They had to be agile and mobile. Leadership was distributed and cooperation was critical to survival as the needs of the group trumped those of the individual. In this system, hoarding and competition within groups were existential liabilities to be avoided and punished. Human activities were local and largely sustainable, despite some mega species extinctions and localized deforestation and landscape change.

The major technological discovery of the Age of Survival was fire, which had a profound impact, providing warmth, protection against predators, and heat for cooking, as well as triggering the development of advanced hunting tools. Fire also allowed humans to become more mobile and migrate farther to more diverse geographies.

Constants Throughout the Ages

Throughout the history of humanity, given the glacial pace of biological evolution, humans have remained broadly constant – driven by the same fundamental needs that influence their behavior. The two basic drivers at individual and societal levels are survival and growth. First we need to survive, which includes procuring food, water, energy, shelter, and physical security and safety. Staying alive and staying safe. Second we need to grow. Physical (or horizontal) growth refers to individual and societal reproduction (population expansion, suburbanization, and colonization), which expands at the expense of other human and non-human populations. Spiritual (or vertical) growth, can collectively be described as the need to flourish or thrive – the need for purpose, creation, connection, self-improvement, and self-actualization. Human consciousness and behavior manifest themselves in different ways depending on how these needs are met within the context and the circumstances of any particular time.

There is evidence of the need for spiritual growth in the Age of Survival – stunning cave paintings in Lascaux (now France), Altamira (Spain), and Serra da Capivara (Brazil) date from 20,000 to 32,000 years ago, long before cities and agriculture.[54] However, the foraging production system did not allow for it beyond the narrow confines of individual and tribal survival – the system represented a hard ceiling to the Age that humans were unable to break through.

During the Age of Survival, estimates suggest that the earth could optimally nourish about 8.6 million people living on hunting, fishing, and gathering,[55] although human populations experienced high volatility, with numbers possibly dropping as low as 1,000 to 10,000 individuals around 70,000 years ago.[56] By the end of the Age, the world's population was probably around four million.[57]

2.2 Humanity 2.0: The Age of Extraction

About 10,000 years ago, some of these groups, first in the Fertile Crescent (Mesopotamia) and then in around half a dozen areas around the world, started the long process of coevolution of cities and agriculture that lay the foundations for future civilizations.[58]

Neither settled communities nor agriculture appeared suddenly and the transition from foraging was far from pre-ordained. Indeed initially, agriculture was inferior to foraging as it offered a lower quality and smaller variety of food for a lot more work. Cities were also inferior in many ways – for example, higher population density (of people, crops, and animals) created the conditions for infectious diseases to spread.

But after millennia of experimentation, city dwellers developed the production and Organizing Systems that brought food surplus, manufacturing, and trade, which enabled them to organize and support greater numbers of people, opening up huge possibilities for humanity. Freed from the need to forage to survive, humans could specialize and innovate in areas like information, food, transportation, energy, materials, and social and organizational structures. Trade allowed plant and animal hybridization techniques to spread, which enabled higher food yields from existing land, which in turn led to larger populations, deeper specialization, and new skills and technologies that expanded the possibilities further. As emerging cities developed, they found new challenges around productivity, monoculture, and overcrowding to overcome, such as disease, pestilence, and the need for food storage and imports to survive seasonality. Those cities with effective Organizing Systems were able to solve these issues, accelerate their expansion, and enable further growth.

The Growth Imperative

As populations continued to grow, the fertile land cities needed for production grew accordingly, driving both the need for new technologies and organizing principles to help conquer, exploit, and manage a larger population and landmass. Extraction became the prevailing system of production and exploitation emerged as a core principle of the Organizing System. Cities harnessed resources and people from as far afield as their technological capability allowed in order to force feed their production systems. They took what they found in nature – plants and animals initially and then other resources – and harvested them to break down, process, and produce the things they needed or wanted, namely food, energy, and materials. Early civilizations thus found themselves inadvertently locked into a competitive system driving an underlying need for growth (the 'growth imperative'). A world of plenty turned into a scarcity-based system of production where the winner takes all.

The key resources in this production system – productive lands, materials, and labor – were available in finite quantities in limited regions of the world. The easiest and cheapest resources to exploit were used first and depleted. Subsequent resources became harder to access and required either increased technological capabilities in extraction or production or the ability to reach and access new resources.

This system of production was a linear model based on harvesting stocks (such as materials and food) and processing large volumes as physical flows. Inputs were constantly required to keep the system operating. Once the growth imperative was unleashed, a self-reinforcing process of predatory competition for control of, or access to, resources was inevitable, and with it the need for military power to exploit land, materials, and labor as rapidly-expanding cities competed with one another for finite resources.

Exploitation and hence inequality became hard-wired into this system. A concentration of the surplus of production was essential to drive growth at the center, generate further specialization and innovation, and support military, technological, and organizational capabilities. Humans were exploited like any other resource – every leading civilization, from Sumer and Greece to Rome and America, was sexist, racist, and xenophobic, serving the needs of a core group. They used forced labor in all its forms, from corvée to slavery, to feed the center and grow their empires.

This model of extraction resulted in a centralization of the system of production, accelerated by the economies of scale inherent within it. Limitations of transportation and communication technologies gave rise to a cluster effect for cities and the centralization of institutions and systems of governance to control and manage civilizations. This centralization was reflected in increasing hierarchies as societies evolved.

Humanity's successful Organizing Systems were no longer based on sharing, generalist skills, and equality, but on ownership, specialization, and inequality. Leadership was no longer distributed but controlled directly from the center. Storage and hoarding were no longer punished but rewarded. Populations that maintained foraging production and Organizing Systems were unable to resist the onslaught from better-organized, extraction-based societies.

The Need for Stability

The growth imperative was, however, counterbalanced by a deep-seated need for stability. For societies to thrive and continue to advance and grow, they needed self-stabilization mechanisms. **Growth without social stability led to disorder and collapse, while stability without growth led to stasis and being left behind.** The Organizing System, through its belief systems, culture, and governance structures, played a critical role in creating the push and pull necessary to balance the need for growth with the need to maintain stability. Finding the balance between these two forces – the yin of stability and the yang of growth – was a critical factor in the success of leading civilizations.

How the balance between 'push' and 'pull' manifested in any civilization depended on the capabilities (technological and organizational) of the core group relative to those they sought to control or influence. For example, Egypt dominated a broad population with powerful belief systems and a strong military, whereas the industrial era has seen the need to empower individuals through political democracy and the freedom to keep the fruits of their labor and own property.

Framework Box 5. Ages, Orders, and Waves

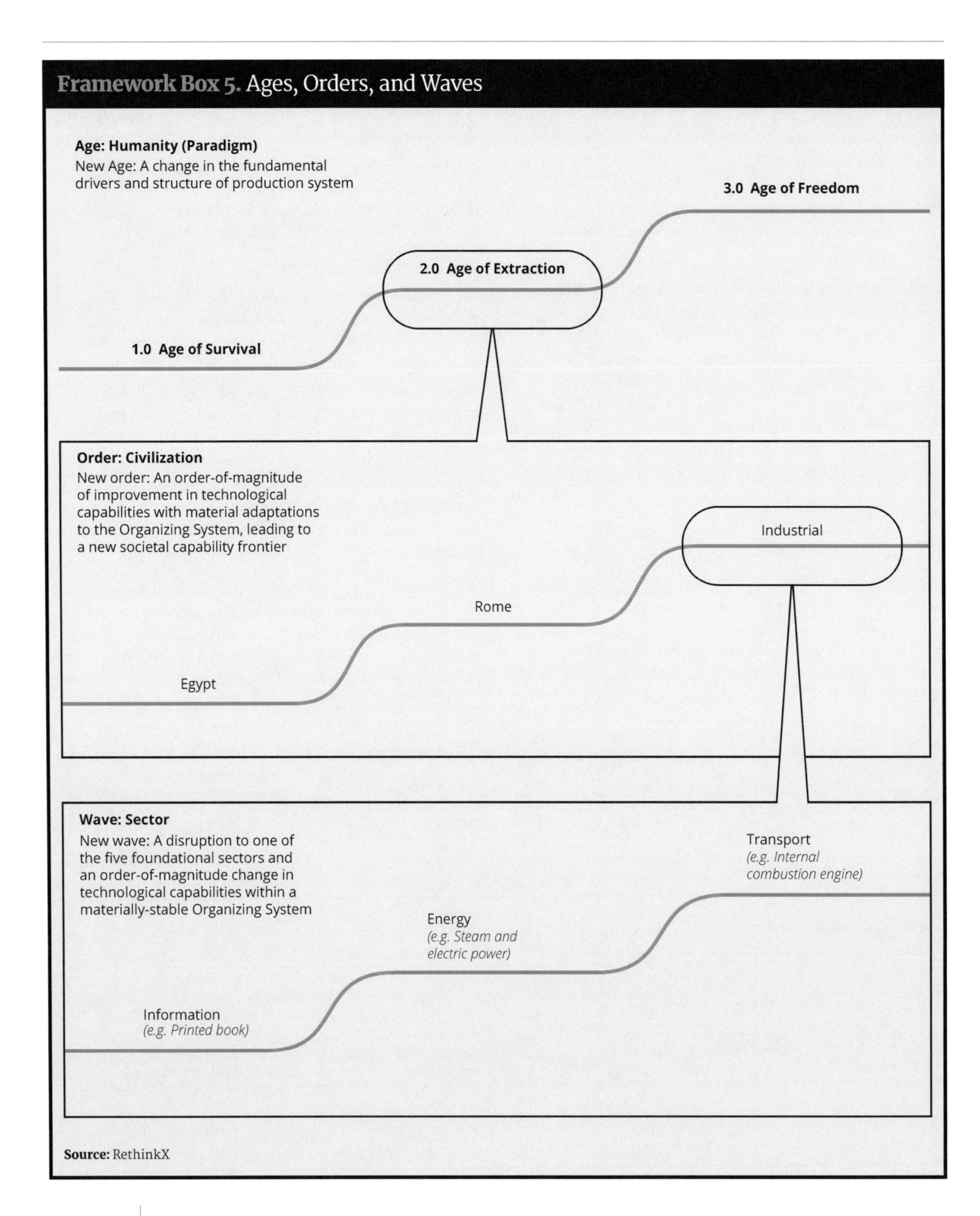

Source: RethinkX

2.3 Rethinking the Lifecycle of Civilizations

Within the Age of Extraction, the arc of human progress has not been smooth or linear but has witnessed long periods of incremental change interspersed with periods of rapid change. This process mirrors those we have seen in sector disruptions, and indeed those within all complex, adaptive systems.

City Size as a Proxy for Societal Capabilities

From the dawn of the Extraction Age, we have seen civilizations advance or decline in a series of phase changes. A crude proxy for societal capabilities is the size of settlement that can be supported by a civilization. The maximum size of city is determined by the technologies and the Organizing System (and geography) of the day. Looking back through history, a recurring pattern is clear to see – large jumps in societal capabilities (core city size) followed by a new equilibrium, followed by collapse into a dark age. Each step up has represented approximately a 10x jump in settlement size relative to the previous high (see Figure 8).

These phase changes represent either a breakthrough or a collapse. Breakthrough as a civilization finds a way to coevolve both production and Organizing Systems that allows it to take an order-of-magnitude advance in societal capabilities, or collapse as it approaches its limits and falls back to a lower order of capability and complexity.[59]

Breakthrough and Collapse[60]

History indicates that order of magnitude improvements in technological capabilities in one or more of the five foundational sectors – information, energy, food, transport, and materials – have triggered cascading waves of technological improvement, creating extraordinary new possibilities across other sectors, the wider economy, and society itself, enabling civilizations to break through previous frontiers to a higher level of societal capabilities.

The periods of societal breakthrough have seen the emergence not just of new technologies, but of a new Organizing System, one governed by new rules with new belief systems, conceptual frameworks, and models of thought to better explain the world, leading to new political, economic, and social systems to influence, control, and manage society.

Figure 8. **Growth in City Size Through History**[61]

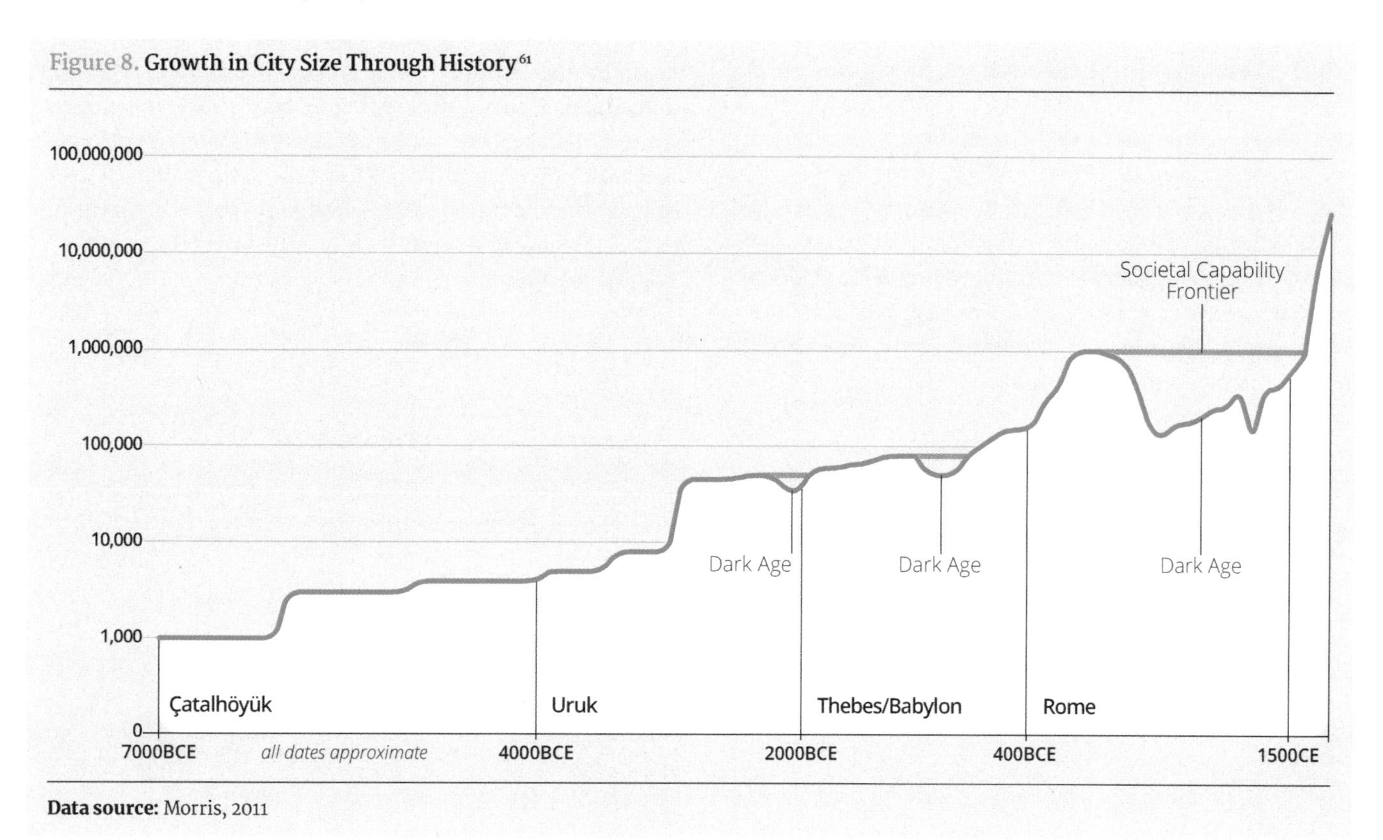

Data source: Morris, 2011

Historically, just as we saw with sector disruptions, these breakthroughs have been led by outsiders with access to, and knowledge of, pre-existing technologies, but without the baggage of incumbency of operating within an antiquated Organizing System and the resistance to change that comes with it. In fact, never has the leader of one order made the adaptations necessary to break through and lead the next, higher order.

Civilizations that harness the right fit of production and Organizing Systems and break through can develop vastly superior technological capabilities. They appear like invaders with celestial capabilities to societies previously out-of-reach and can overwhelm those still operating under a now outmoded Organizing System. For example, the Chinese empire, which had far surpassed European powers through the Dark Ages, was brought to its knees in 1842 by a small squadron of British ships. In the same way, Roman legions arriving on the shores of the British Isles 1,800 years earlier or the Spanish conquistadors arriving in the New World appeared as inconceivably powerful.[62]

After breakthrough follows an expansionary phase. As their scale and reach grow, civilizations can no longer sustain themselves locally but require an expanded region of control or influence from which to harvest the energy, food, resources, taxes, and wealth necessary to support them.

While civilizations are expanding geographically, riches and resources flow in increasing quantities to the center, generating the wealth needed to improve living conditions and maintain the support of a growing core population. But as the geographic limits of their production and Organizing Systems are reached, these riches and resources dry up, with diminishing (or negative) returns to further expansion as control or influence of far flung provinces becomes increasingly expensive and ineffective. Without this increasing surplus from expansion, growth begins to slow. The emergence of rivals with similar capabilities can exacerbate this problem.

At a certain point in their expansion, civilizations pass a threshold and enter a 'buffer zone,' within which they can still survive or even thrive for relatively long periods of time. However, with their centralized, brittle structure, they have limited ability to react to shocks that impact their productive capacity and ability to sustain themselves – single points of failure that render the whole inherently fragile. These shocks can be environmental, military (wars and invasion), socio-political (inequality or over-exploitation leading to rebellion or civil war), or pandemics. Environmental shocks can be exogenous (historically), such as changes to climate and rainfall patterns leading to drought or inundation, or they can be self-inflicted, such as decreasing soil fertility caused by over-irrigation, soil salination, deforestation, or intensive farming, all of which affect the ability of a civilization to feed itself. Over-exploitation of scarce resources can likewise impact energy or material supplies. As they reach the limits of their geographic spread, civilizations can no longer expand to exploit more land or resources to overcome these shocks.

The impact of the end of the expansionary period can be compounded as narrow, embedded interest groups (religious, warrior, monarchical, commercial, or aristocratic) seek to improve their position further. Without the easy gains from expansion, they increasingly extract rents from within society, aided by Extraction Age economies of scale that lead to a centralization of wealth. These groups can capture governments at many levels to privatize and concentrate wealth and profits, while socializing risks and waste. The end result is an extractive feedback loop where more profits accrue to these interest groups. The end result is a concentration of profits and wealth in fewer hands, an increase in inequality, and a decrease in social cohesion and support.

As the system becomes more centralized and leveraged, it becomes less robust and more unstable. Progressively smaller shocks can threaten its very existence. The openness to new ideas and people that helped it succeed in the past, by encouraging diversity of thought and the exchange and fertilization of ideas, reverses and acts as a constraint on change and adaptation, resulting in a failure to make the changes necessary for long-term survival – Organizing Systems harden at a time when they need plasticity to adapt. The faster change happens, the more unstable the system becomes, which leads to an increasing desire for social stability and maintaining the status quo.

And herein lies the fundamental flaw with all civilizations in the Age of Extraction. The extractive, exploitative, winner-take-all production system is concerned mainly with maximizing income from useful outputs for the center. Both the finite nature of resources and the human and social impacts from production (described today as externalities) are ignored. Indeed, civilizations that go too far in correcting for them handicap themselves competitively in the long term compared with those that do not, creating an inherent conflict between short and long-term interests. All previous leading civilizations were blind to the long-term effect of these impacts until it was too late, prioritizing the short over the long-term and the narrow over the common interest.

Without the possibility of geographic expansion, growth can only come from breakthrough – order-of-magnitude improvements in technological capabilities and a new Organizing System that allow civilizations to produce more from their existing footprints. The only other choice is to cut consumption to live within the existing system's means, which is almost impossible to do voluntarily when the fundamental beliefs, institutions, and reward systems that led to its success are based on driving growth. Indeed, these two options are in direct conflict – cutting the scale of production reduces the surplus available to support the investment in innovation needed to break through.

This is the context for collapse. As ever in a complex system, there is seldom simple, linear cause and effect – change comes from the complex interaction of all parts of the system. While the proximate cause of collapse is often pandemics, invasion, social unrest, long periods of drought or environmental degradation,[63] the context has been set far earlier – namely a civilization that has passed the limits within which it can sustain itself and has lost the ability to adapt at every level.

Civilizations soon enter a death spiral. Reductions in the productive capacity reduce the surplus available to feed the core power structures, such as the state bureaucracies, and economic, military, and religious elites. As the surplus shrinks, social expenditures such as education, water, health, social services and technology development are cut, leading to a reduction in support for the system and further lowering of productive capacity. In the face of collapse, rather than adapt, civilizations have tended to re-double their efforts on what had worked previously – more extraction, more walls, more blood sacrifices, or more power for the center of authority, be it king, emperor, or the elites that endorse them. Such actions, while positioned as solutions, are Band-Aids on a system on the verge of collapse. More than that, they accelerate the breakdown by exacerbating the very problems that are causing it. The negative feedback continues as taxes and debt increase and currencies are debased, selling the future to pay for the present, further destabilizing an already brittle and unstable system.

Every leading civilization, from Çatalhöyük and Sumer to Babylon and Rome, has collapsed in this way, unable to adapt and break through the capability frontier of their order. Dark ages followed, representing a reversal of social complexity and a collapse to a lower level of capabilities. This process of collapse happens remarkably quickly – all the leading millenary civilizations in the Fertile Crescent and Eastern Mediterranean world collapsed in just one hundred years (between 1250 and 1150 BCE), many of them never to return.[64]

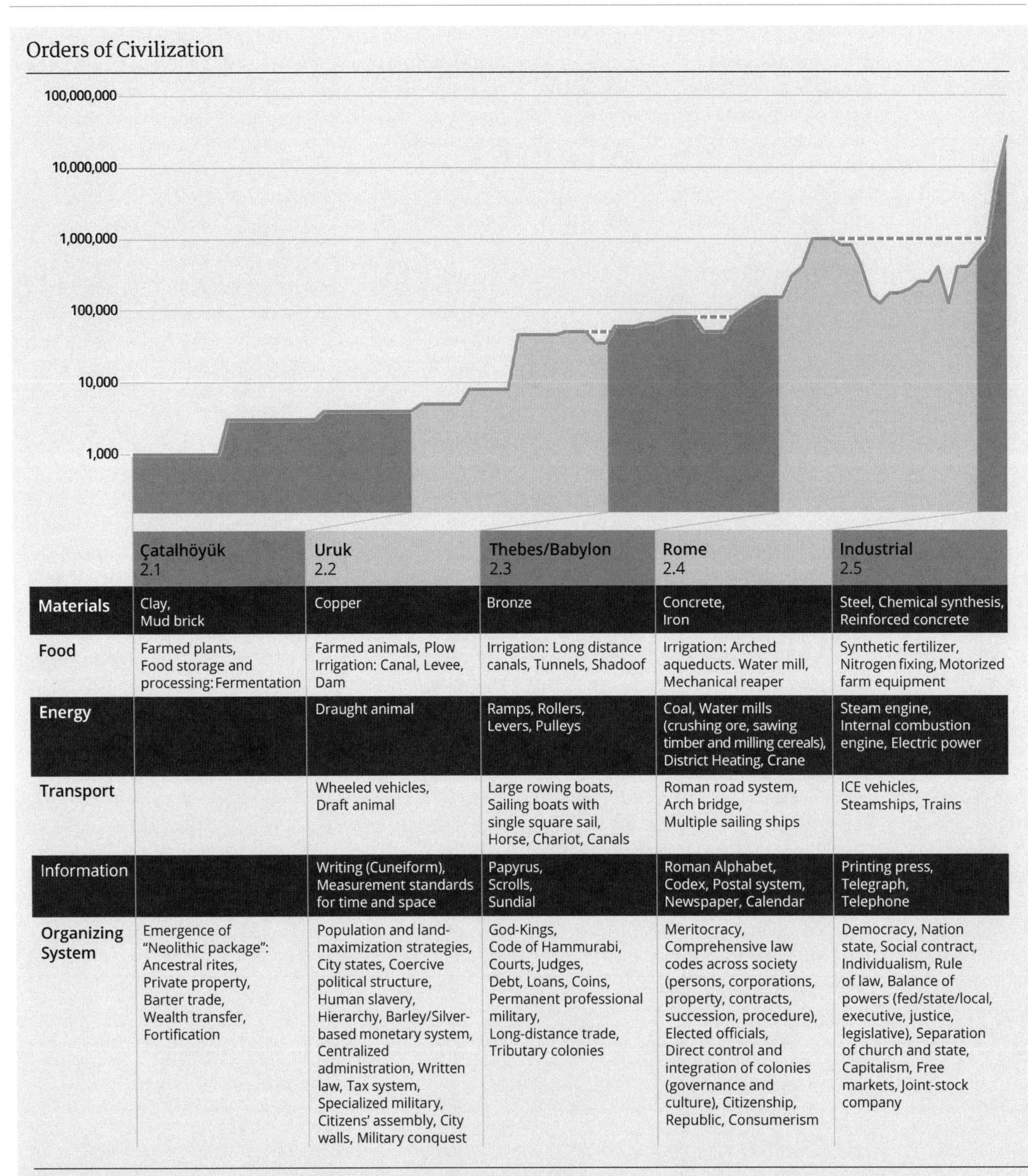

	Çatalhöyük 2.1	Uruk 2.2	Thebes/Babylon 2.3	Rome 2.4	Industrial 2.5
Materials	Clay, Mud brick	Copper	Bronze	Concrete, Iron	Steel, Chemical synthesis, Reinforced concrete
Food	Farmed plants, Food storage and processing: Fermentation	Farmed animals, Plow Irrigation: Canal, Levee, Dam	Irrigation: Long distance canals, Tunnels, Shadoof	Irrigation: Arched aqueducts. Water mill, Mechanical reaper	Synthetic fertilizer, Nitrogen fixing, Motorized farm equipment
Energy		Draught animal	Ramps, Rollers, Levers, Pulleys	Coal, Water mills (crushing ore, sawing timber and milling cereals), District Heating, Crane	Steam engine, Internal combustion engine, Electric power
Transport		Wheeled vehicles, Draft animal	Large rowing boats, Sailing boats with single square sail, Horse, Chariot, Canals	Roman road system, Arch bridge, Multiple sailing ships	ICE vehicles, Steamships, Trains
Information		Writing (Cuneiform), Measurement standards for time and space	Papyrus, Scrolls, Sundial	Roman Alphabet, Codex, Postal system, Newspaper, Calendar	Printing press, Telegraph, Telephone
Organizing System	Emergence of "Neolithic package": Ancestral rites, Private property, Barter trade, Wealth transfer, Fortification	Population and land-maximization strategies, City states, Coercive political structure, Human slavery, Hierarchy, Barley/Silver-based monetary system, Centralized administration, Written law, Tax system, Specialized military, Citizens' assembly, City walls, Military conquest	God-Kings, Code of Hammurabi, Courts, Judges, Debt, Loans, Coins, Permanent professional military, Long-distance trade, Tributary colonies	Meritocracy, Comprehensive law codes across society (persons, corporations, property, contracts, succession, procedure), Elected officials, Direct control and integration of colonies (governance and culture), Citizenship, Republic, Consumerism	Democracy, Nation state, Social contract, Individualism, Rule of law, Balance of powers (fed/state/local, executive, justice, legislative), Separation of church and state, Capitalism, Free markets, Joint-stock company

Data sources: Morris, 2011, Encyclopaedia Britannica, Ancient History Encyclopedia
Note: This table includes innovations not at the point of invention, but at the point when they were meaningfully adopted. Furthermore, inventions are included against the civilization that broke through to a new order. For example, a number of Greek inventions are listed under Rome because they came after the Egyptian high-water mark and formed part of the Roman Order.

The Çatalhöyük Order (ca 8,000 BCE-): Humanity 2.1

Trade and the domestication of plants allowed small bands of hunter-gatherers to settle in fertile regions and grow their settlements to thousands of people, supported by relatively simplistic organizing principles. Early settlements were likely to have been hybrids combining elements of foraging and agriculture. Village size was limited both by the distance that could be traveled on foot and by the organizational limits imposed by word-of-mouth communication and collective human memory.

The Sumerian Order (ca 3,500 BCE-): Humanity 2.2

Early agricultural societies improved plants through selective breeding and domesticated animals to provide (and store) food, energy (draught animals), and transportation. As new technologies such as the wheel and plough and new materials such as copper and bronze were harnessed, adopted, and improved upon over many centuries, and as methods of food production became more efficient and larger areas of land were exploited, societies became more capable and could support increasing numbers of people.

Writing (cuneiform) was a key innovation – one of the most important in history. By preserving information, it enabled the improvement of all other technologies. The original Farmer's Almanac contained instructions on the best way to plant, irrigate, and care for crops. Sumerians invented measurements for land (the iku – which begat the acre) and time (60 second minutes and 60 minute hours). New models of thinking emerged that better explained the world around them, helping to underpin ever-more complex and far-reaching technological and organizing capabilities. These advances enabled the Sumerians to break through the capability frontier of the previous order and sustain cities of tens of thousands of people.

The Babylonian/Egyptian Order (ca 2,200 BCE-): Humanity 2.3

Technological breakthroughs in the use of iron, the development of irrigation, the pulley, larger rowing boats, early sail boats, and chariots allowed goods and people to be transported ever farther. The development of the map and a legal system that provided for private ownership of property, money, and trade, alongside improvements to writing, papyrus, and scrolls, allowed these civilizations to organize and control ever-larger regions. As a direct result, cities grew beyond 100,000 individuals.

The Roman Order (ca 1 CE-): Humanity 2.4

See box below

The Industrial Order (ca 1,500-): Humanity 2.5

See below

The Emergence of Rome[65]

The Roman Empire provides an instructive example of this historical pattern. Following the collapse of Egypt and Babylon, the leaders of the previous order, the Eastern Mediterranean powers collapsed into a dark age. In a gradual process of advancement, the Phoenicians and then Greeks developed new ways of understanding the world as Axial thought emerged. Advances in mathematics, science, philosophy, and astronomy created new possibilities for understanding and organizing societies. New materials were harnessed as bronze gave way to more powerful iron-based civilizations. The power of the watermill (an energy technology invented by the Greeks) was used to grind grain. The mechanical reaper was used to increase agricultural productivity, concrete and cast iron (materials) were used to build superior roads and bridges, and better ships (transportation) were used to bring cheaper and more abundant food to the city from the corners of the Empire. Roman information and communication technologies facilitated trade as the Roman alphabet, far simpler than Cuneiform or Hieroglyphic, became standard. Development of the crossbow, catapult, and improvements to chariots, as well as new combat strategies, dramatically improved military capabilities. Rome created the world's first postal service, the bound book (codex), and the newspaper (Acta Diurna), as well as a new standard (Julian) calendar. Organizational improvements through experiments with democracy, systems of taxation, and governance through direct control of colonies, along with a culture that inspired awe, combined with all these technological advances to help Rome break through the capability frontier of the previous order and establish the most successful civilization the world had ever seen.

The Collapse of Rome

Rome's extraction-based Organizing System meant it had to keep growing its territory to feed the center. However, once its societal capabilities reached their limits, further growth had negative returns and endangered the stability of the whole system. Limited data on the size of the Roman Empire indicate that it reached its limit at around 4.5 million km^2[66] – every time it breached this limit, it had to pull back. For example, feeding a population of one million required hundreds of square miles of tillable land, far in excess of what the Italian Peninsula could offer, so Rome invaded North Africa to gain access to more land and human labor (slaves) to feed its center. Most of the grain that fed Romans was now shipped from Carthage and Alexandria.[67] Rome's transportation and logistical capabilities were unsurpassed, but this centralized, command-and-control, monocrop architecture was structurally unstable and brittle. Carthage and Alexandria provided two single points of failure – capture either port and the whole Roman Empire was under threat.

Over the course of two centuries, a combination of factors, which individually would not have proved fatal, converged to critically weaken the Empire and set the context for collapse, including a move to a wetter, less stable climate that affected food production, regular pandemics, political infighting, and increasing inequality. Political, social, economic, and environmental instability grew until the system ruptured in around 395 CE. The Empire was broken up into two parts and Rome itself went on to collapse ignominiously.[68]

Landmass Controlled by Rome
(km^2)

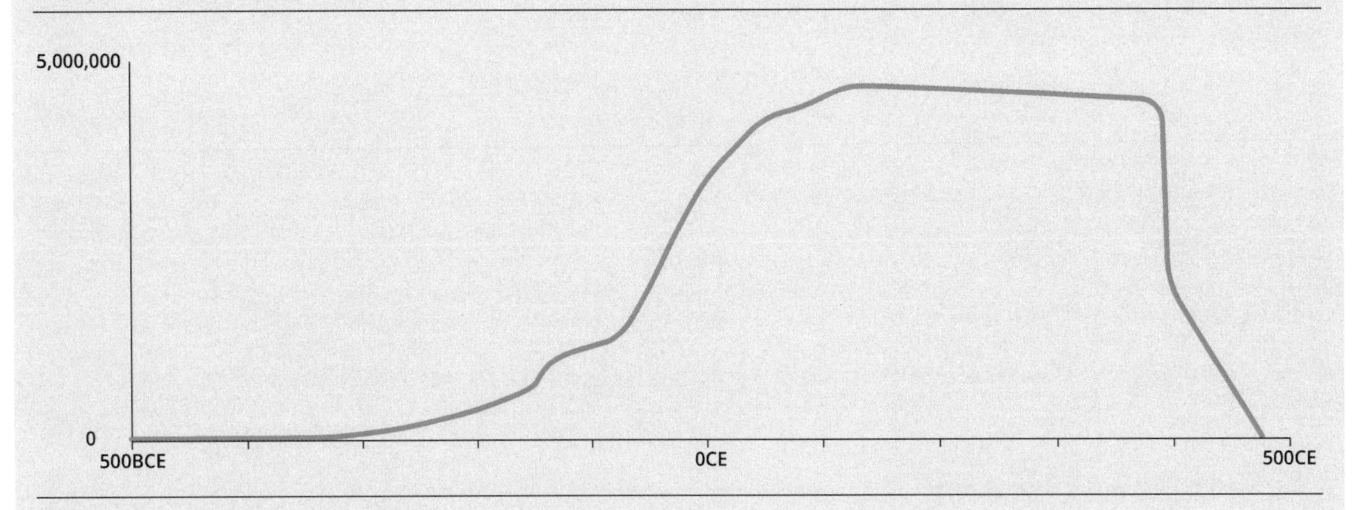

Data source: Taagepera, 1979

Framework Box 6. Change at Civilization Level

A civilization can be pushed out of equilibrium as the brakes that resist change and maintain stability weaken and are overwhelmed by the forces for change. At this point, there are effectively only two options: break through to a higher order or collapse. History indicates that breakthrough can only be realized with order-of-magnitude improvements in technological capabilities. Breaking through to a higher order requires self-organization, exploration, experimentation, and a willingness to renounce obsolete organizing principles – all without any guarantees. The only certainty is that rejecting change will lead to collapse and a new dark age.

The process of change mirrors that at a sector level:

» Breakthrough is driven by convergence – dramatic improvements in technological capabilities in foundational sectors to create the potential for an order-of-magnitude improvement in societal capabilities.

» Civilizations that develop the best combination of technology and Organizing System increase their capabilities rapidly and outcompete others.

» Over time, the Organizing System becomes more embedded and less adaptable.

» As civilizations reach the limit of their expansion, the context is set for collapse and the baggage of incumbency prevents the adaptation needed to break through.

» A shock to the system, such as environmental degradation, increasing inequality, or increasing financial and social instability, can push it out of equilibrium and lead to collapse.

» Civilizations lose adaptability as they approach collapse, blinded by incumbent mindsets, beliefs, incentives, and interests. They double down on what brought them to greatness instead of adapting to the new reality.

» The existing system collapses before the new one emerges. This manifests in a dark age that can last for hundreds of years.

» These periods of change represent a phase change.

» Change happens quickly.

» The emerging leaders come from the edge of the old system.

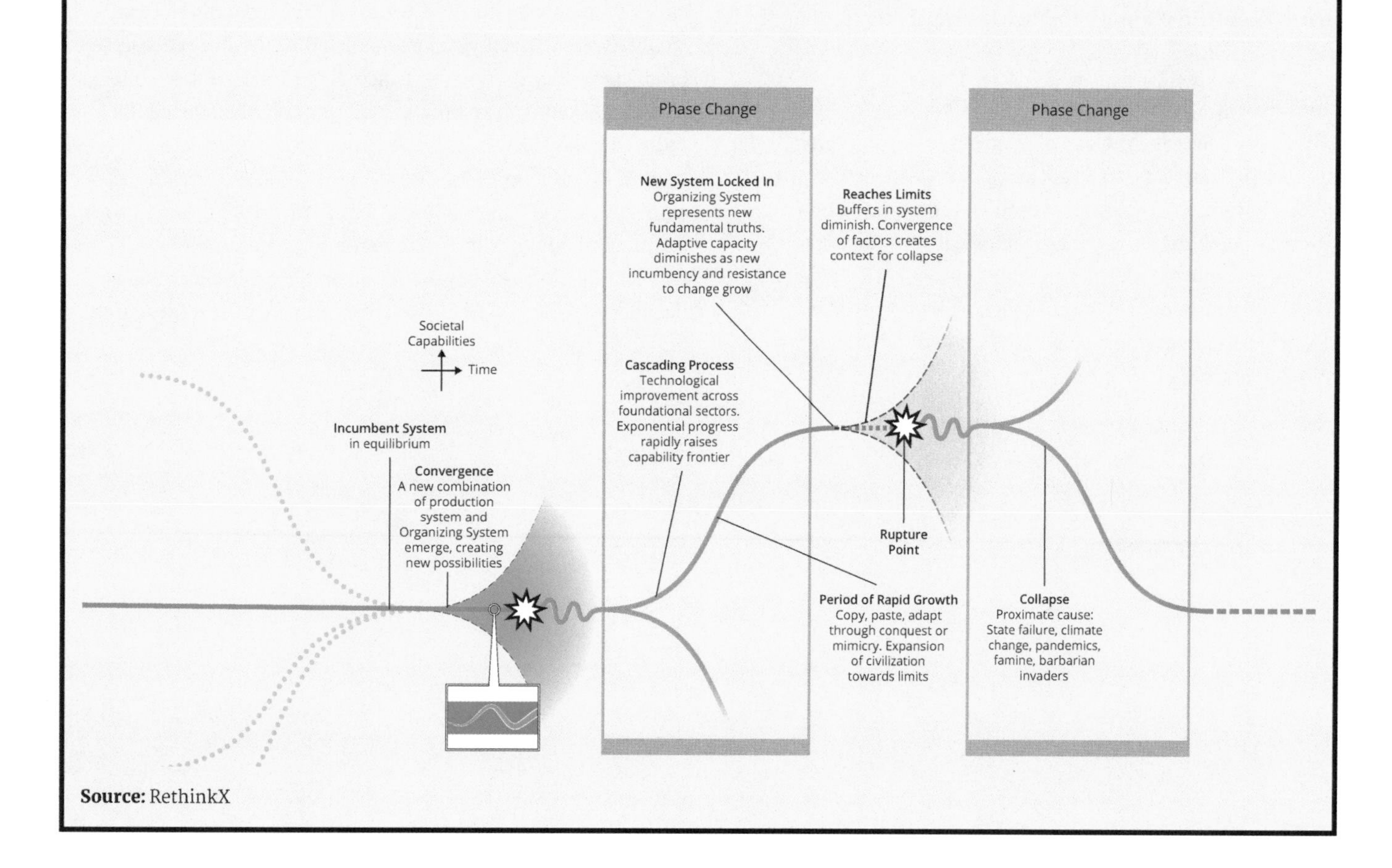

Source: RethinkX

The Emergence of the Industrial Order

As the Roman Empire collapsed, the Mediterranean basin and its hinterlands plunged into a new lower order known as the Dark Ages. Technological and organizational capabilities regressed dramatically as Europe fractured and was overwhelmed by religious dogma, poverty, violence, and ignorance. For centuries, even the ruling elites, including emperors, kings, and knights, were illiterate. From the 8th to the 10th centuries, Europe's main export commodity was its own people – enslaved humans.[69]

Nearly a thousand years after the collapse of the Roman Empire, new ways of thinking slowly emerged within pockets of medieval societies to question the stifling religious dogma and better explain the world. New conceptual frameworks emerged alongside new political, social, and economic constructs and helped drive some extraordinary technological innovation that underpinned a new mechanized system of production.

Parallel improvements in materials (iron then steel), energy (the steam engine), transportation (railways and steamships), and food unlocked previously unimaginable possibilities across the economy, leading to cascading waves of technological improvement that transformed society. The new industrial production system that emerged ushered in a new civilization that, by 1800, finally broke through the capability frontier of the Roman Order.

Cascading Technological Progress

This first wave of technological progress of the emerging Industrial Order was catalyzed, as we have seen, by the printed book. Plunging costs of information and communication opened opportunities to a far greater swathe of the population to participate in the sharing and development of knowledge. It was a platform on which subsequent developments in scientific understanding were built that laid the foundations of the Industrial Revolution.

While the first printing presses were small and distributed, small print runs of perhaps 100 copies turned into much larger print runs of 500 copies or more. Economies of scale pushed the system to become more centralized, as profitability required more copies of each publication to be printed. The invention of the telegraph and telephone then allowed for direct, person-to-person communication.

The spread of information was a 'push' model, with publishers deciding what would be published centrally before distributing information widely. A newspaper industry emerged in the 18th century with the same structure, driven by the same economic realities. High costs of infrastructure, scarce distribution channels, and economies of scale led to centralization and high barriers to entry. As a result, large newspaper groups controlled the flow of news. The emergence of radio and television followed the same model of centralized access to consumers, providing a degree of control over the flow of information. Centralized regulation controlling a limited number of channels emerged to match this structure – governments could regulate newspapers, TV, and radio and influence the messages they delivered.

Progress in the other foundational sectors followed a similar model. Steam power developed as Thomas Newcomen and then James Watt developed a viable new energy technology – the steam engine. This invention enabled the creation of disruptive products across many sectors including transportation, mining, energy, agriculture, and manufacturing and kickstarted the Industrial Revolution. This age of machines relied on fossil fuels to power production – first coal, then oil and gas. Steam ships, trains, cars, and planes allowed access to the whole world with an order-of-magnitude improvement in speed and range. A centralized system of production on a greater scale than ever before emerged to harvest, extract, and process resources and to distribute the resulting outputs.

The Industrial Order Organizing System

In a process of coevolution, the Industrial Order Organizing System emerged alongside this extraordinary technological progress. New models of thought, belief systems, and conceptual frameworks from the Renaissance and Scientific Revolution gave rise to new political, social, and economic systems that, together, grew to influence, manage, and control the actions and behaviors of hundreds of millions of individuals across the world. The need for scale, reach, centralization, and hierarchy that defined the industrial system of production was reflected in the industrial governance structures, institutions, and in geopolitics.

Religion, which had served a purpose both in explaining the world and in governance through the Dark Ages, no longer offered a competitive advantage. It was unbundled and replaced by empiricism and democracy, its purpose shifting to providing social compliance, a sense of purpose, and stability. Those states that separated church from state and embraced scientific thought progressed far faster than those organized around religious dogma. Like the tailbone or appendix, obsolete remnants of human evolution, Organizing System relics of earlier orders often remain. Occasionally they flare up, cause damage and are surgically removed but, in general, their importance diminishes in leading nations – monarchies remain, stripped of their absolute power, and religious and racist dogma fight to return to an imagined golden era.

Scientific thought sought to explain the world by breaking it down into ever smaller pieces, focusing on simple, linear cause and effect. This reductionist thinking, which could explain the separate parts of the world down to a sub-atomic level, was well-matched to the emerging technologies and system of production. It was reflected in education, industry, science, academia, government, and in the increasing specialization of labor, as the complexity of the whole was broken down into manageable parts, disciplines, or departments.

Medieval governance structures and institutions were overturned as an increasingly educated, informed, and empowered population demanded rights long denied.

This growing resistance to the prevailing hierarchical and constraining socio-political structures provided the context for the emergence of the key guiding principles, tenets, and organizational institutions that we hold so dear today, such as individual rights, democracy, capitalism, free markets, trade, the separation of church and state, and nation states.

Governance structures evolved to mirror the attributes of a globalized production system. Scale and reach mattered and provided competitive advantage, so city states and principalities in Europe evolved into nation states – the predominant organizing structure of the order. No one country needed direct control of every other nation, merely the power with allies to exert enough influence to ensure access to resources and markets. Global governance structures, institutions, and agreements also evolved to cover issues that required cooperation beyond national borders, but these were designed to further the interests of the nation states' centers of power, not to replace them.

Over time, nation states became ever-more embedded, inspiring bonds of loyalty through shared history and experience, language, culture, and beliefs, to the point where their existence appeared unquestionable to their citizens. The limits of transportation and communication technologies meant bonds of kinship were local, with loyalty owed to a country as a 'tribe'.

Democracy emerged as the best-adapted system of governance, enabling self-organization, experimentation, competition, and adaptive decision-making. It allowed election on the basis of merit (to some degree) rather than inheritance. It enabled the removal of those that failed to perform or acted against the communal interest and enshrined the individual rights of citizens in a way that maintained support among a wide populace, even in difficult times. A series of checks and balances emerged to provide stability and certainty for longer-term decisions and ensure that radical change was difficult. These elements of democracy allowed some flexibility in decision-making and ensured, in theory, that leaders put aside their own interests for the greater good in a way that monarchs did not.

'Winning' in the emerging industrial production system required encouraging innovation, investment, and hard work from a far broader swathe of a population that was increasingly educated in the new ways of thinking. No longer could a small core dominate the wider population through violence, fear, or a belief system that bred subservience (push). New systems that focused on the pull of reward and incentives and the perception of individual freedom outcompeted other alternatives.

Widespread private ownership of property, the rule of law, and free-market capitalism thus emerged as the best economic fit for the industrial production system. Free markets allocated resources, labor, and capital and, while not entirely efficient, performed far better than centralized decision-making alternatives. This system encouraged innovation, investment in the future, and risk-taking as individuals were able to keep more of the gains of their endeavors, all of which helped drive growth. Experiments with other forms of ownership floundered by killing the incentives to invest in growth.

The need to incentivize growth within a framework of resource scarcity led to a tension between tolerating (or encouraging) inequality to drive growth and the need for social cohesion. Successful societies managed to maintain the support of both an expanding core and the exploited masses in order to survive by redistributing wealth to maintain stability.

The social contract that emerged allowed individuals to trade their labor for capital and offered some form of safety net and growth opportunities to most citizens. This contract allowed millions of people to self-organize, start new businesses, and drive the system of production at vast scale. It created the incentives and security to invest in the development of their skills and knowledge, driving specialization and growth at all levels.

This winning formula for the new Industrial Order emerged over a long period of time. It was not a planned or linear process – technology, Organizing Systems, and geography each influenced the development of the other to determine the winners, until ultimately this Order organized, managed, influenced, and impacted the activities of people at a global scale. In many ways, this process was self-catalytic.

Why America, Leader of the Industrial Order?

The U.S. started industrializing towards the end of the 18th century and by the end of the 19th century the tide had shifted decisively in its favor. Like Europe, it too had advantages of geography – huge scale, productive farmlands, navigable rivers, and critical resources, made more accessible by the advent of coal, hydro, and gas-powered electricity and the development of trains, cars, and planes. But just as the European powers began to resist change, America embraced it, driven by an entrepreneurialism and an openness to new ideas and people[70] – except for the Chinese Exclusion Act, the U.S. had open borders until the 1920s. It also had the advantage of being separated from its geopolitical rivals by two large oceans and having two militarily-weak neighbors, meaning it could invest in its own growth rather than protecting itself against aggression. The Northern Europeans, however, reorganized into nation states, and with rivals at their doorsteps with similar capabilities, descended into internecine war and carnage.

Today, while the U.S. itself does not directly control the world in the way historical empires did through colonization, it is first among equals in a system that does – influencing, subjugating, or incentivizing the whole planet to operate within its model.

In essence, the core of our Organizing System today is the same as that which emerged at the outset. The extraction DNA has remained largely intact while making incremental adaptations to improve societal capabilities. As with all previous civilizations, the extraction system of production continues to work in favor of a core demographic, while exploiting other groups. In the U.S., for example, "we the people" initially meant "we the Anglo, white, male landowners." As the country expanded, it needed a larger core to maintain stability, so membership was extended to demographics that had previously been excluded – first other Northern Europeans and then Southern and Eastern Europeans, non-landowners, and women. The Constitution allowed for an expansion of rights through amendments, but not all groups given rights by the Constitution were invited to be members of the core population.

Part 3

Rethinking the Present: Between Two Ages

3.1 A New Age: From Extraction to Creation

The Extraction Age, which started with Neolithic villages harvesting a small landmass in the Fertile Crescent, now encompasses billions of people with a footprint that covers the whole planet.

Geographically, there is little scope to expand. The final flourishing of this Age, the Industrial Order, has seen societies experience extraordinary growth in their capabilities, but we are beginning to reach the limits of our civilization and enter the buffer zone. Early signs of breakdown are apparent, manifesting in a growing number of societal, governance, and environmental problems across the world.

The impact of our civilization on the Earth's biophysical systems has gone beyond the limits of what can be supported sustainably as, like previous civilizations, we prioritize short-term growth over long-term survival.[71] Climate change, soil degradation, deforestation, and increasingly unstable ecosystems are the result. Our food system has reached its limits as we push to extract ever more from our finite land while externalizing the social costs of environmental degradation and pathogenic viruses. As geographic expansion grinds to a halt and new competitors emerge (see China box opposite), the surplus that flowed back to the U.S. and its allies through their expansionary phase is diminishing. Powerful incumbents are becoming ever-more entrenched and protective of their position, extracting rents from all parts of society. Governments, which are in place to regulate companies on behalf of the people, are now regulating people on behalf of companies, amplifying the trends of increasing inequality, disillusionment, and dwindling institutional trust.

However, a new system of production is emerging with the potential to break through the capability frontier of our current order and solve the root cause of the problems we are experiencing. With geographic expansion no longer possible, order-of-magnitude improvements in technological capabilities offer the only way to break through. This is exactly what we are seeing today. Numerous technologies are improving at an exponential rate and disrupting every sector of the industrial production system. This technological progress has the potential to create extraordinary increases in our societal capabilities. An entirely new system of production is emerging that will decrease dramatically our dependency on resources and the environment by an order of magnitude or more, increasing the robustness and stability of those societies that embrace it. As a result, climate change, inequality, and many of the other serious problems society faces today can be solved.

Technology Convergence and the Rise of China

Like previous civilizations, as the U.S.-dominated Industrial Order has spread around the world, America has extracted enormous wealth from the regions it has controlled or influenced. Extraordinary growth through the 20th century saw the U.S. produce and sell its products and services to almost every country on Earth, with the resulting profits flowing back to the center.[72] But the system is reaching its limits, with little further geographic expansion possible. Indeed over the last 30 years the dynamics have begun to shift as new competitors have emerged, in particular China.

The convergence of the container, personal computer, and internet has disrupted manufacturing supply chains in advanced economies and pushed down the cost of transporting goods by 10x, to the point where the importance of geography is vastly diminished. Shipping costs across the Atlantic have gone from $420/ton in the 1950s to less than $50 today, while shipping time has gone from months to days.[73] Indeed the cost of container shipping has dropped so low that "economists who study international trade often assume that transport costs are zero."[74] Combined with distributed computing and instant communications, a just-in-time manufacturing supply chain has become possible. Manufacturing goods can now be packaged, rerouted – just like internet communication packets – and reassembled anywhere in the world. With transportation costs falling to near zero relative to the cost of goods, assembly lines for cars, electronics, and even food can now be designed around the world. Suppliers in Shanghai or Shenzhen can compete with manufacturers in Michigan or California to provide car or electronic parts to the auto industry in Detroit or computer industry in Silicon Valley.

China's rise has coincided with this technology convergence. To catch up with the U.S., China copied and pasted the American Organizing System, with only minor alterations. Experiments with Special Economic Zones (SEZs) and free-market, capitalist-oriented labor, management, and trade structures allowed China to benefit from its huge untapped, low-cost labor market. Today, seven of the world's ten largest container shipping ports are in China, which now leads the world in the production of electronics, cars, and consumer goods.[75] The jobs and part of the wealth that flowed back to the U.S. now remain in China. What started as a business-to-business, manufacturing supply chain disruption has now moved to a new phase – business-to-consumer commerce disruption. Millions of China-based manufacturers now sell directly to U.S. consumers without ever setting foot in America.[76] The U.S. has responded in traditional fashion by subsidizing interest rates, increasing leverage, and printing money to keep a semblance of growth alive – making its economy more brittle and unstable.

This process has contributed to many of the social and economic issues in the U.S. today. In the meantime, China has seized on the opportunity to increase its societal capabilities and become the world's manufacturing powerhouse.

3.2 The Creation-based System of Production

We have made enormous technological progress since the dawn of industrialization, but in terms of what is possible – the limits set by the laws of physics – we have barely begun.

We are now entering a period of extraordinary technological disruption – change at a speed and scale far beyond that which any civilization has experienced before. Whereas disruptions historically have been relatively slow-moving and isolated, the 2020s will see disruptions affecting every sector of the economy concurrently.

As has always been the case, the catalyst for disruption is the extraordinary improvement in a number of key technologies (see Figure 9) that each have the potential to impact multiple sectors of the economy. Just as we have seen with the smartphone and the car, investment and improvement in any one sector improve the cost and capabilities of the underlying technologies and help to disrupt other sectors. For example, as batteries improve as demand and investment in electric vehicles rise, they become competitive in the electricity storage market, which boosts the market for solar and wind energy, which increases demand for more grid storage, which catalyzes further improvement in battery technology cost and capabilities, which improves EV competitiveness relative to fossil-fuel powered vehicles. These technologies are converging in different combinations in different sectors to enable extraordinary improvement in the costs and capabilities of new products and services. As disruptions unfold and reinforce one another, their impacts will ripple out across society, profoundly changing our world.

Of the five foundational sectors that will trigger this extraordinary transformation, information is the most advanced, just as it was when the Industrial Order emerged.

Figure 9. **Key Technologies, Convergence, and Interaction Between Sectors**

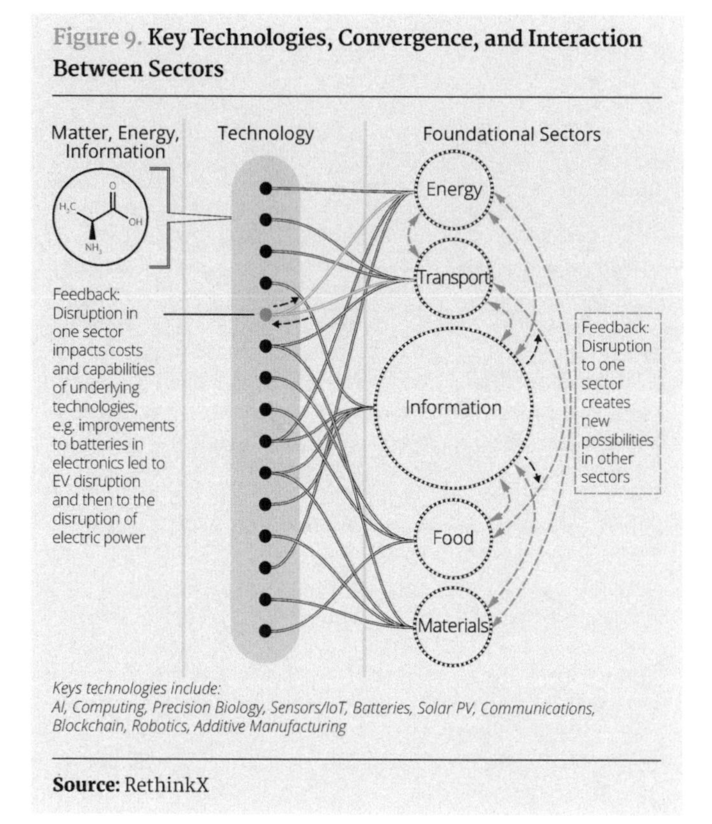

Source: RethinkX

Information and communications: Extraordinary advances in information processing and communications have already led to plummeting costs, which have dropped towards zero as billions of people have been connected and empowered with tools that would have been unaffordable a decade ago and unthinkable two decades ago. The smartphone, as we have seen, was a key enabler, creating extraordinary new potential across all sectors of the economy.

Twenty years ago, the idea of having a large proportion of the population work, study, and socialize remotely was the stuff of science fiction and Silicon Valley futurists. The recent Covid-19 crisis shows that the information and communications technology to make this happen is already largely in place. But not every job can be performed from home. Factory or warehouse work, for example, requires humans to be onsite. However, the cost and capabilities of many key technologies such as sensors, communications, computing, 3D visualization, and robotics are expected to improve by several orders of magnitude over the next decade. As technology allows for an increasing portion of physical work to be performed remotely (via virtual, enhanced, or mixed reality), this labor could be sourced from anywhere in the world, before ultimately being replaced by automation. Over the last 20 years, we have seen white-collar labor become digitalized (so-called business process outsourcing) and manufacturing physically outsourced to low-cost labor markets. Over the next decade, we will see a similar trend for blue-collar labor (factory process outsourcing), with physical production occurring locally and labor performed remotely. The implications across the economy are profound – where we live and work can be almost completely decoupled. The impact of this on immigration, border controls, tax regimes, labor regulations, and even on concepts like nationalism, are extraordinary.

Figure 10. **Food: From Foraging to Extraction to Creation**

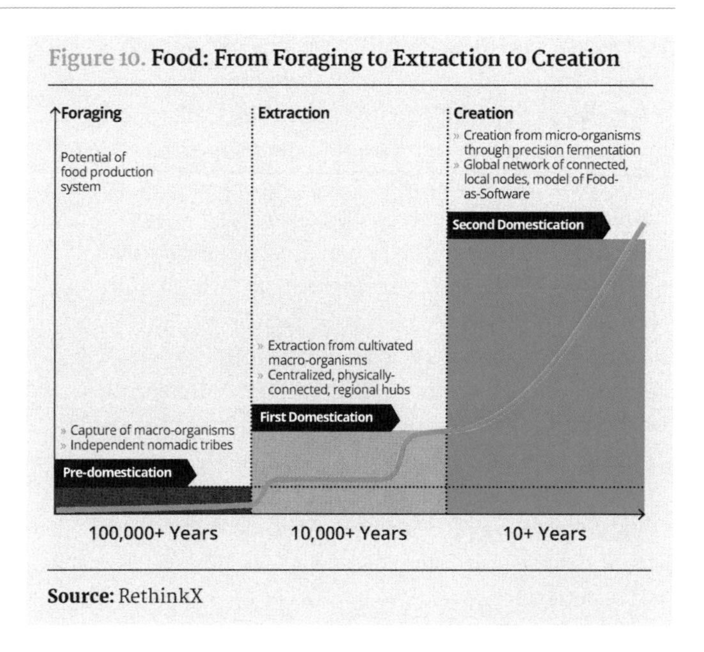

Source: RethinkX

Food: Harnessing biology through precision fermentation (PF) will lead to the end of animal agriculture, representing a second domestication of plants and animals (details are laid out in our *Rethinking Food and Agriculture 2020-2030* report). Nutritious food that initially replicates livestock proteins (milk and meat) will not just be an order-of-magnitude cheaper, but superior in every possible way – the food itself (taste, aroma, texture, mouthfeel, nutrition, and variety), predictability of quality, price, and supply, as well as impact on health, animal welfare, and the environment. Food production will shift from a model of extraction, where we grow plants and animals to break them down into the things we need, to a model of creation, where foods are built up from precisely-designed molecules and cells. The DNA of a single soy plant or chicken will be enough to create an unlimited quantity of soy or chicken protein. Small biological reserves with immense biodiversity will, therefore, be far more valuable than immense tracts of land with marginal biodiversity. Costa Rica, for example, will be more valuable for food, materials, and medicine than the entire U.S. Midwest, while Brazil and Indonesia are destroying a future of infinite possibilities by tearing down their forests for short-term gains.

This emerging food system will have profound impacts as the 70% of agricultural land and water currently used for animals is largely freed up for alternative uses. This is not a one-for-one replacement of the few dozen animal proteins currently in our food supply – using precision biology, we can design a nearly infinite variety of proteins (and other complex organic compounds including lipids, vitamins, and biologics) with precise specifications, including nutrition, taste, texture, color, and impact on health. A Food-as-Software model will allow scientists, food designers, and molecular chefs to develop food like we develop smartphone Apps. Individualized nutrition, where specific proteins, fibers, and vitamins are developed on-demand to match our specific genetic, epi-genetic, and metabolic makeup as well as lifestyle will become the norm. Many of the biological technologies developed for food production will also have applications in healthcare, cosmetics, and material production.

Energy: Solar power, batteries, sensors, and AI will enable a new energy system that is distributed, with demand predictively managed to match supply. Energy will be generated mainly through solar PV (complemented by wind), which is already the lowest cost form of energy and is disrupting the new-build, grid-scale, fossil fuel-based generation market.[77] In fact in many markets, the total cost of solar PV is already below the marginal cost of fossil-fuel and nuclear electricity. Distributed energy generation combined with distributed battery storage will replace the centralized electric power system, as localized production eventually costs less than the transmission and distribution costs of a centralized energy system. Existing fossil-fuel plants will see their utilization rates drop as zero marginal-cost solar, wind, and battery power grows, effectively used only to cover ever-shrinking gaps in demand. Within a few years, as the economics of these conventional plants deteriorate further, they will essentially be stranded, so we may need to selectively and temporarily subsidize some of them while the accelerating build-out of new clean energy infrastructure catches up with demand.

Figure 11. **Individually Owned (IO) ICE, IO EV, and TaaS Costs (USD/mile)**

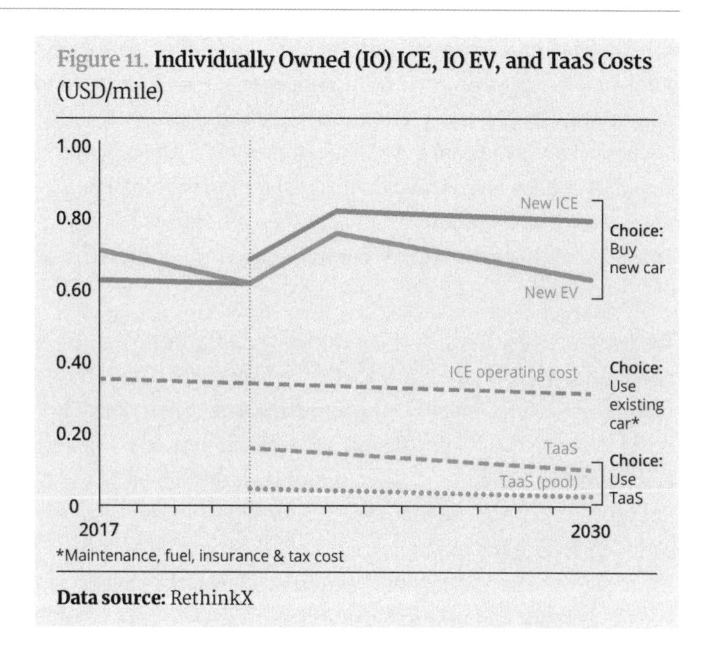

Data source: RethinkX

This vastly more distributed system will allow energy to be produced anywhere, at any scale, and will provide power at a total cost approaching 1 ¢/kWh and negligible marginal cost. Peaking power plants will be rendered obsolete as battery storage flattens both the demand and generation curves (destroying volatility-based pricing power) and provides more predictable, higher quality, and resilient electric power. Even the concept of baseload generation will disappear as central generation is replaced by a network of smart, on-demand generation and storage resources. The collapse of GE's power division, which bet on a fossil fuel, centralized power generation future, is the shape of things to come.[78] Indeed the existing centralized system is facing a death spiral of increasing costs, lower demand, and bankruptcy as utilization rates drop and demand migrates off grid.

As the virtuous cycle of clean disruption gains momentum, fossil fuels and fossil-fuel technologies will enter a vicious cycle that will also affect the heating market. The fossil fuel industry's diminished scale will make heat more expensive, leading companies to replace it with cheaper, more predictable solar and battery technologies, leading to further erosion of fossil fuel markets, leading to more expensive industrial and space heat, leading companies and consumers to drop fossil-fuel heat altogether.

Transportation: Transport will be disrupted in myriad ways (details are laid out in our *Rethinking Transportation 2020-2030* report). TaaS (shared A-EVs hailed on demand) will rapidly replace the model of individual car ownership and with it the combustion engine. Electric vehicles (trucks, vans, buses, and cars) can drive half a million miles (soon to be one million) as opposed to around 140,000 miles for ICE vehicles. This means fleets will also have to go electric because the per-mile cost of EVs is one third (soon to be one sixth) the cost of ICE transportation in high-utilization models. Companies like Amazon and Fedex will have no choice but to quickly replace their whole fleets with electric trucks and vans for purely economic reasons.

As human drivers are replaced, congestion will ease and the possibility of integrating other electric forms of transport (scooters, drones, and bikes) will emerge. Together, these disruptions will deliver a transportation system 10x cheaper and far more efficient than the one it replaces. As the speed of transport improves in congested areas, this new system will create possibilities to change where we live and work, transforming the layout of cities and towns. Its impact will ripple out across trains, logistics, aviation, oil, climate change, and geopolitics. Just like the ICE car did 100 years before them, new modes of transportation will restructure culture, entertainment, and commerce.

Materials: Production of materials will be transformed in the same way as food production, moving from a breakdown to a build-up model. Just like the chemical and petrochemical industries disrupted plant and animal-based materials and created a panoply of materials that did not exist in nature, so new technologies will disrupt extractive resources and chemical synthesis by creating a near-infinite array of materials with hitherto unheard of capabilities at a fraction of the cost and resource utilization of extraction-based methods. Indeed, precision biology and PF are to the 21st century what the chemical and petrochemical industries were to the 20th century. Together with CRISPR, additive manufacturing, and nanotechnologies, they will allow us to manipulate matter,

Figure 12. **PF Disrupting More Industries as Costs Fall**
Log ($/kg protein)

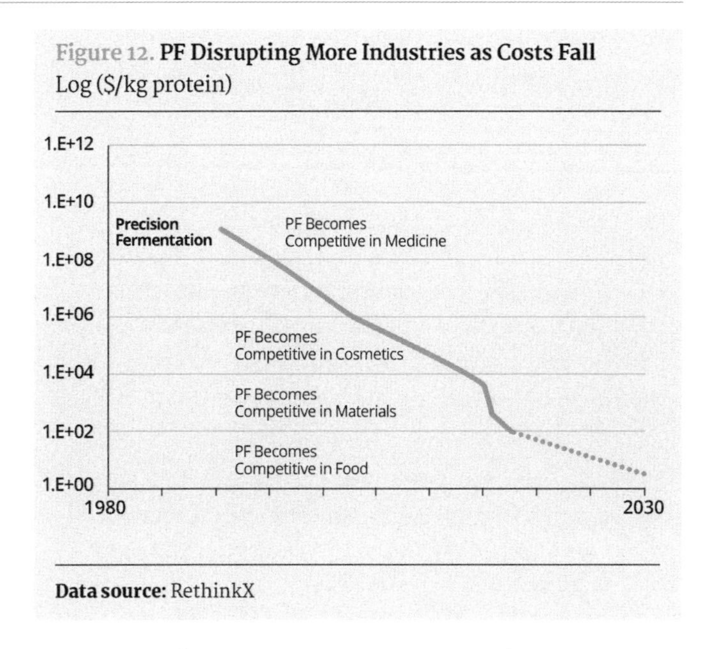

Data source: RethinkX

energy, and information at smaller scales with far greater efficiency to build materials with combinations of properties that are stronger, lighter, and more flexible, all with minimal waste. As these technologies improve in both cost and efficiency, resource scarcity could become a thing of the past.

These material disruptions will not be a simple substitution of new materials for old. Modern materials will disrupt sectors and transform society in unexpected ways. For example, as the cost of solar PV drops below the cost of building materials (such as structural plywood), the line between construction and energy will blur.[79] As builders use PV as building material (because it is cheaper), the effective cost of electricity will be zero or even negative.

The extraordinary improvements in the costs and capabilities of modern technologies mean that these sector disruptions are inevitable. Driven by powerful feedback mechanisms, these sectors and all others will be transformed through the 2020s and into the 2030s at a speed and scale that almost no present-day analysis predicts. Together, they represent a new system of production that could ultimately deliver a new age.

3.3 Humanity 3.0: The Age of Freedom

This emerging, creation-based production system opens up the possibility of an entirely new age – the Age of Freedom.

This is not a third or fourth industrial revolution as the mainstream narrative implies. The emerging system of production, and the civilization it will enable, will be based on fundamentally different drivers and attributes to those of the Extraction Age – a difference as profound as the shift from foraging to agriculture and cities, but condensed into a fraction of the time.

The creation-based system of production will be unlike any other in human history. The current, large-scale, centralized system will be replaced by an entirely decentralized system based on a model of resource creation, not extraction. A model of build-up, not breakdown. We will build what we need from the ground up at the molecular level, with an order-of-magnitude improvement in cost and efficiency. The building blocks of this system – the bit (and qbit), photon, electron, molecule, and DNA (or gene) – are available and plentiful everywhere and can be recombined in infinite ways to create new products and services at essentially zero cost.

This new production system is based on increasing returns and near-infinite supply, as opposed to the diminishing returns and scarce, geographically-constrained supply of the Extraction Age. A creation-based system can produce near-infinite outputs once the infrastructure is built – limitless quantities of organic materials (food, clothing, and materials) produced from the genetic information held in single cells and the plentiful flows of energy produced from the sun, with just a few further inputs. Such a system produces only what is needed, without the need to grow whole plants or animals or dig up huge quantities of raw materials to break down into useful outputs. Stocks of non-organic materials (e.g. metals) and capital will be needed to seed the system, but everything else can be created and sourced locally.

The Network and the Node

As communities, towns, and cities become self-sufficient, able to produce much of what they need to meet their basic needs locally, a system of production will consist of independent nodes connected to scale-free, complex information networks. This structure is likely to be mirrored in successful Organizing Systems, with governance at all levels.

Billions of producer-consumers will generate their own energy, develop novel foods, materials, and products, and exchange blueprints and ideas globally, with physical production and distribution occurring locally. The massive flow of physical resources across borders will be replaced by flows of information, transforming trade relations and geopolitics. For example, a new electric transport system will face hugely diminished geopolitical and security risks. Lithium, nickel, and cobalt, key inputs for today's batteries, are stocks, whereas oil is a flow – without lithium, the existing vehicle fleet can continue to function, but without oil, it grinds to a halt. The same goes for food, energy, and materials. As physical flows diminish, capital flows through the economy will also plummet, with profound implications for investors, credit, and monetary systems. As we move from a system of production based on extraction to one based on creation, therefore, the competition for scarce resources that drives the growth imperative will inevitably decline.

This networked structure will create a far more robust and resilient system than the existing centralized, hierarchical structure – no longer will a shock to one part of the system imperil the whole. As we see in biology, impacts to individual or multiple nodes within modular, networked systems do not ripple out through the entire system.

The emerging age will see a reversal of the extractive trend of increasing supply-side scale, reach, and centralization. The advantages of scale will disappear as we move from a top-down, hierarchical, extractive society to a bottom up, connected, creative one. Scale as a competitive advantage will be replaced by demand-side network effects. Small communities, cities, regions, and states will compete on equal terms with countries small and large. This should come as no surprise given the historical precedents. The UK and Holland were small countries that used Industrial Order technologies and Organizing Systems to dominate the world. The difference today is that new capabilities allow even small start-ups to compete successfully with large corporations or even governments.

Network centrality will be critical for communities to thrive and participate in the emerging production system. Societies that develop Organizing Systems based on network dynamics will be several steps ahead, while attempting to bolt the network to existing command-and-control, centralized, extraction-based Organizing Systems is a recipe for disaster. In tandem, independent governance structures will need to grow up around these nodes.[80]

As the emerging, distributed, networked system increasingly overwhelms the center, the extractive core will collapse. Not only is creation a vastly superior production system, but networks themselves make it easy to weaponize information to empower individuals and institutions to destroy the center, which will be so weak it will offer no resistance.

The Incompatibility of the Industrial Organizing System

This new, empowered, distributed, resilient production system is running headlong into the hierarchical, centralized, brittle Industrial Order Organizing System. In the same way that the invention of the printed book helped to catalyze the collapse of the Medieval Organizing System, progress in information technologies is already creating the conditions for the collapse of the Industrial Order. The Industrial Order Organizing System evolved alongside, and was well-adapted to, the large scale, centralized, extractive technologies of the last 200 years. It complemented well the drivers of the Age of Extraction – growth, scale, and reach. However, it is completely incompatible with the new creation-based system of production and will become increasingly unable to govern, manage, and control society.

Indeed trying to understand, manage, and influence our economies and societies through this industrial relic will not only exacerbate the problems we already face, but create new problems, accelerating the collapse of our civilization. Political divisions, inequality, and social instability will worsen dramatically over the next decades. Governance and decision-making, likewise, will become increasingly ineffective. This combination of widespread discontent and an inability to understand and lead will push many more people towards the kinds of simplistic, extremist, populist solutions that are increasingly taking hold today.

Institutional failure to understand the processes of change and recognize the possibilities opening up means we are trying desperately to patch up our industrial Organizing System, rather than creating the conditions for a new system to take its place. Indeed the speed and scale of change and the growing uncertainty it breeds is triggering an immune response from our current system, with calls to double down on outdated and inappropriate solutions – the modern-day equivalent of more sacrifices, more priests, and more walls. These solutions are merely Band-Aids on a system that is inherently unstable, fragile, and unsustainable.

Framework Box 7. Information: From Extraction to Creation

As we have seen, the Industrial Order information system was born out of key technological innovations such as the printing press, telegraph, telephone, radio, and television. Extraction Age scarcity and economics pushed the system to centralization – a top-down model of controlled, one-way flows where information and knowledge were gathered and distributed through centralized channels to 'passive' consumers. The infrastructure, governance, and regulatory structures were built out to reflect this structure, leading to 'natural' distribution monopolies.

But the development of the personal computer, internet, and smartphone transformed the model. Suddenly, anyone, anywhere connected to the network could communicate with anyone else. Economies of scale vanished and with them barriers to entry. A model emerged of infinite supply with bottom-up, distributed, empowered producers and consumers connected via a global information network. Information economics, network effects, and increasing returns have replaced extraction economics, economies of scale, and decreasing returns as the key driver of competitive advantage. Costs of communication and access to information dropped to near zero, creating new possibilities in how we think about ownership of intellectual property and how we communicate ideas. Barriers to entry also fell away – entrepreneurs in a garage (Google), dorm (Facebook), or apartment (Uber) could now start a company that has instant access to billions of consumers and producers globally, disrupt whole industries and even governments, and be valued at one trillion dollars in just 20 years.

Creation-based Production System vs Extraction-based Organizing System

Facebook has a population of 2.5 billion people – larger than any country in the world. It has the capability to wage information warfare to change the national narrative (formerly a role of national governments and before that of kings, emperors, and church) and trigger regime change without firing a single bullet.

Again, we can learn from history, for Facebook is the modern-day equivalent of the British East India Company (EIC). Both developed organizing capabilities to capture the opportunities created by technology convergence, capabilities that surpassed not just those of their private competitors (such as WeChat or the Dutch East India company) but also of leading nations. The EIC was a joint-stock company (a new concept at the time) that moved from trade and commodities to politics and territory at the start of the Industrial Revolution. The EIC toppled governments with its own military and extracted labor, commodities, and taxes from some of the largest nations on earth. At its peak, it minted its own currency, was responsible for half the world's trade and had a military twice the size of Britain's[81] – it could probably have toppled the British government had it decided to stop feeding London and turn its guns on the UK instead of Asia.

Just like the British government with the EIC, legislators today do not understand Facebook. For the best part of a decade, they have been asking the same question – is it a publisher or a technology platform? They have talked about breaking the company up but how do you break up a Freedom Age information network with a legal, financial, and regulatory framework that is designed for the Extraction Age? Until we develop new organizing principles, including legal frameworks and novel digital asset classes and ownership structures, we will not be able to manage and govern this information system. Should we create a new type of legal entity (say, IN-corp for Information Network corporation) with a totally new set of legal, financial, and intellectual property rules? How should we treat ownership of personal data, currently privatized and owned by the platforms? Should the IN-corp be a new asset class, owned and operated for the benefit of the network? All these questions will need to be addressed.

The new information system is also disrupting politics, with profound implications. President Trump came from outside the political establishment (the edge) and beat candidates of both major political parties to become the nation's commander in chief. The old information establishment would probably have filtered out his message, but every centralized institution (newspapers, broadcast television, political parties, and the justice system) was unable to stop his deft use of social media and its rules of direct engagement. These new rules and success metrics have allowed Trump to govern by communicating directly with his base, bypassing established Industrial Order rules. These rules were considered constants but, just like every aspect of an Organizing System, they are in fact variables. This is not the first time technology disruption has impacted politics – as we have seen, the printing press enabled information to flow directly from the edge of the centralized religious establishment to create a political disruption that engulfed Europe for hundreds of years.

Architecture of the Ages

	Extraction	Creation
Model of production	Extract (plant, animals, fossil fuels, metals, materials, land, people) break down and process. Repackage	Create from building blocks in nature (photon, electron, DNA, molecule, bit/qbit). Self-replicating once seeded
Based on	Scarce, depleting resources	Locally-abundant resources (e.g. seed stocks of metals)
Key requirement	Reach and scale to harness key physical resources	Key physical resources available locally. Self-sufficient communities
Causing	Huge global flows of physical commodities (e.g. industrial cows, oil, metals) and physical goods (with embedded knowledge). Limited local production of physical goods	Huge global flows of digital knowledge, huge local goods production (with high embedded knowledge) and flows of physical goods. Limited global physical commodity flow
Cost	Inefficient, high waste, high cost	Efficient, low waste, low cost
Key Driver	Zero-sum predatory competition leads to growth imperative (exploit or be exploited). Dysergies (1+1<2)	Little competition for physical resources. Synergies (1+1>2)
Economics	Extraction economics – diminishing returns. Supply-side economies of scale	Information/Network economics – increasing returns. Network effects
Leads to	Centralization and concentration of production	Distributed, modular production
Geography	Geography important for competitive advantage	End of geography as determinant of competitive advantage
Architecture	Centralized, brittle, fragile. Single points of failure	Network and node. Robust, resilient
Governance	Centralized, hierarchical, unequal. Need for military to protect access to scarce physical resources and trading routes	Distributed (node), global (network). Diminished need for conquest and military protection of physical resources and trade flows
Flaws	Growth imperative that drives inequality and environmental degradation (externalities), systemic booms and busts, and predation of resources	Ownership of network/platforms. Data ownership/surveillance. Weaponization of information, biology and (artificial) intelligence
Kinship	Exclusionary, binary, analog: local, racial, religious, national	Inclusionary, multi dimensional, digital: community based on evolving common interest globally
Work	Specialization Forced labor	Generalization Rights to needs

Source: RethinkX

3.4 Industrial Order Band-Aids and Creation Age Possibilities

Trying to explain, understand, and manage the world by the old Extraction Age rules, structures, and beliefs is futile.

Almost every conversation today about fixing societal problems is rooted in this linear mindset. Like doctors treating individual symptoms and causing all manner of side effects while ignoring the root cause of illnesses, the solutions suggested right across the political spectrum, whether they be economic, political, social, or environmental, are all aimed at patching up the current Industrial Order Organizing System, somehow finding a way to make it function effectively in a rapidly-changing world it is no longer suited to.

Within the extraction paradigm, the problems are in conflict. Solving climate change in a system of extraction requires hugely negative social impacts. Solving inequality kills the incentives to technological progress. Solving the nutrition crisis requires more land, more animal farming, and more deforestation, giving rise to more zoonotic virus epidemics, in a system already pushing humanity to its limits.

The solution is not to fantasize about turning back the clock and reinstating a mythical past, which some extremist groups and populist movements desire, or use Industrial Order regulatory measures (tax, redistribute, or behavior change) to solve these problems, as populist movements suggest. The problem is far more profound – our civilization is reaching its limits and the current Organizing System is crumbling, increasingly unsuited to the emerging system of production, unable to understand or manage society and, as a result, acting like a straitjacket on our individual and collective potential. Its lack of flexibility means it cannot adapt quickly enough and an increasing resistance to fundamental change means we risk being locked into a system that ceases to enable continued technological progress and becomes increasingly unsustainable – socially, politically, economically, and environmentally. The prelude to an inevitable collapse.

Social Instability

Inequality in the Age of Extraction has been caused by a production system based on exploiting scarce resources and the economies of scale that act to centralize wealth. Owners of the system of production and of scarce resources in the Industrial Order could extract rent at the expense of the rest of society.

As our civilization reaches its limits and these incumbent elites capture more of the surplus, wage growth stagnates, inequality grows, and populism, discontent, and dislocation rise. These problems are exacerbated as our social contract, which trades labor for capital and social stability, breaks down in the face of increasing technological disruption. The evidence is there for all to see – the four biggest political democracies in the world (India, the US, Indonesia, and Brazil) are all governed by populist leaders, while the re-emergence of centralizing extremism, be it political, religious, or economic, continues to gather pace around the world. These movements push back against progress, as openness to new ideas and people diminishes as we look to assign blame for our problems. Rising racism and xenophobia are signs of this process.

Inequality and instability will only grow through the 2020s and early 2030s as every sector of the economy is disrupted. We have seen from previous disruptions that the collapse of incumbent industries and the dislocation that comes with it happens early, while the creation of new industries and jobs and the benefits that come with them follow later. As incumbent industries collapse over the next decade and leadership is unable to understand why, let alone anticipate and mitigate the impacts, we will face more unrest and social dislocation around the world, leading to more extremist, centralizing, populist movements.

Indeed extreme inequality is inevitable if we continue with our current ownership structures, as network effects, driven by the winner-takes-all dynamic, replace economies of scale as the primary driver of competitive advantage (see Ownership in the Age of Freedom box opposite). Ownership (capital) will take an even greater share of the economy at the expense of labor, resulting in ever-greater concentration of wealth and influence. **Those who control the information network and the platforms built on top of it will own the system of production.**

The Band-Aid (Industrial Order) Solution

Solutions suggested today, such as taxing and redistributing more, protecting jobs, re-training, limiting consumption, or putting up protectionist barriers are merely Extraction Age solutions to Freedom Age problems. Relying on redistribution alone to offset inequality and unemployment

Ownership in the Age of Freedom

The Achilles heel of information networks in the Industrial Order is ownership of the network itself. As we have seen with Facebook and its ilk, ownership of the network confers great power – far more than supply-side economies of scale. As the information network and the production platforms that run on top of it take an ever-increasing share of economic activity, and as the system of production becomes more digitized, continuing to manage our economic system through our current ruleset might well lead to a new kind of extractive inequality, orders of magnitude worse than we see today. **Those who own the information networks will own both the system of production and the Organizing System – a dangerous combination.**

Decisions about ownership of the network and the core platforms built on it, and about intellectual property rights, personal data, and open access to information, will determine whether the outcome is benevolent or dystopian. For instance, in our Food and Agriculture report we explain how the cost of protein using creation-based production methods will be 10x cheaper than current extraction methods. But cost is not price. If we allow the modern, Food-as-Software production network to be dominated by healthcare-style monopolies, the benefits of the immense improvement in cost, quality, and variety of modern foods will not necessarily accrue to humanity but rather to a few biotech companies. A transparent, collaborative, open-source system more closely resembling software development than current drug development and marketing is not just preferable, but perhaps an existential choice for humanity.

We therefore need new models of thinking for the network, including new organizing principles, new conceptions of ownership and management models, and new asset classes. The principle of the joint stock company and the derivative corporate legal entities that helped Europe to organize its colonial expansion and extraction will need rethinking for a creation-based production system. What worked for the British EIC and Dutch VOC is not what we need in the Age of Freedom.

will become increasingly ineffective. In some cases, particularly limiting consumption, these so-called solutions are counter-productive and dangerous, hampering economic growth and destroying the capital required to build the emerging system of production, leading to further social unrest and, ultimately, societal breakdown.

New Possibilities

The creation-based system of production will see the cost of our basic needs – energy, food, water, communications, transport, education, shelter, and healthcare – fall towards zero. Within a decade or two, a new social contract providing a right to all our basic needs will be possible and affordable – a step on from the concept of universal basic income (that is indefinitely unaffordable to the linear mindset). As a result, our notion of work, jobs, income, and incentives will change dramatically. We will no longer have to work to survive and so the need for 'jobs' as we know them will disappear. Work will be re-imagined as we are increasingly free to pursue other activities. Our reliance on and relationship with central government will change dramatically.

Freedom from economic want, from the fear of survival, becomes more than a possibility – it becomes a choice. History shows that the narrow freedom to vote in the Industrial Order does not imply freedom from hunger, fear, violence, precarity, or homelessness. Real freedom – the freedom to spend our time creatively, spiritually, purposefully, free from the drudgery of providing for ourselves – will emerge to replace the incomplete freedom of political democracy. We will need to rethink how we spend our time and find purpose and fulfillment in the new age.

This will reframe entirely the political debate. In many ways, the politics of the Extraction Age has been a struggle between the need to incentivize growth and the desire to ensure the fruits of extraction are shared equitably. We have, in fact, tolerated a level of inequality in order to incentivize growth. Blanket redistribution (communism/socialism) means incentives to grow disappear and societies fall behind. Too little redistribution (unfettered free markets) and inequality and social upheaval results.

But if all our basic needs can be provided for negligible cost, **inequality will no longer be the price of growth. Social violence and extreme waste will no longer fit the winning production system.** The Gordian knot will be cut. The tension between growth and stability that has favored the most successful socio-economic system of the Industrial Order – free-market capitalism with some redistribution and safety net – will become obsolete. Full participation in, and access to, our economic surplus and communal ownership of the network will become possible while maximizing competitive advantage.

A new social contract and new ownership and market models, that improve rather hinder competitiveness, raises other possibilities too. In a world where everyone has the potential to meet their needs easily, where they have equality of access and opportunity to participate creatively however they choose, where everyone can live their whole life without fear or despair, will hoarding matter? If the floor is raised to a level where all can thrive, will we care about the ceiling?

Governance

The process of democracy is being hijacked as elections are influenced by interest groups and even foreign governments that corrupt the truth and target voters with false or misleading messages through social media. Fake news, fake analysis, pseudo-science, and an inability to manage the flow and accuracy of information undermine trust in the democratic process. The decentralization of information technology and social media in particular enables citizens to lock themselves in echo chambers, leading to a splintering of society and a polarization of opinion, making the agreement required to effect change ever harder to reach.

Just as we need the ability to make bold decisions and react to rapid change, our decision-making processes are seizing up, gridlocked by the capture of narrow interest groups and political division. The desire for certainty in increasingly unstable times is creating resistance to change. The very checks and balances that are hard-wired into our constitutions and decision-making processes to create the stability needed to succeed in the Industrial Order are now millstones round our collective necks, stifling change just as it is needed most.

Political institutions based on centralized hierarchies are becoming increasingly obsolete as citizens have access to as much or more information and expertise than governments themselves. Indeed many governments are now democracies in name only (DINO). Electoral processes that were designed for people to choose representatives now see politicians choosing their voters.[82]

Adding to the problems of democracy and decision-making will be the increasing irrelevance of the unit of governance within which these processes work – the nation state. In the emerging network-first world, hierarchical, centralized nation states will become far less relevant.[83] As the need for scale and reach is replaced by localized self-sufficiency, nation states will face being outcompeted by governance structures better suited to the emerging age, namely the network and the node.

As trust is transferred to the network and the node, tribal loyalties will necessarily shift from the center. Loyalties might be owed to those in our immediate vicinity, either physical, spiritual, or intellectual, with shared beliefs, values, and interests. Indeed, many people already have far more in common with others scattered across the Earth than with those inhabiting the same block.[84]

The Band-Aid Solution

In the face of these multiple threats, governments the world over are looking to consolidate power by increasing their control over individuals, corporations, and states. Established democracies are doubling down on a centralized model that is no longer fit for purpose, epitomized by the federal administration's increasing attempts to push back against progress in California in areas such as clean energy, transportation, and pollution. Equally, the response of government to attempts by hackers to interfere with the electoral process has been to clamp down on the social media companies, not other governments who finance and manage weaponization of information.

Countries using Industrial Order Organizing Systems cannot understand, let alone regulate, tax, or control a company (or country) using creation-based production and Organizing System capabilities. This can be seen in attempts to regulate Google, Facebook, Amazon, and others. As we have seen, how can a single country, particularly one that does not understand network dynamics, regulate a company like Facebook? How can it tax them effectively when they are more adept at moving information than the state (money is information, after all)? Breaking up these information platforms is not the answer. It is an Industrial Order solution in a Freedom Age world.

We see further evidence of this mismatch in failed attempts to prevent a handful of hackers with a small budget perverting democracy to enable regime change in the most powerful country in the world. Individuals in a basement or garage are becoming empowered with the tools to cause havoc, capable of hacking power grids and financial institutions, creating viruses, or taking down information networks.

New Possibilities

Nation states governed by political democracy are supposed to help provide society with efficient decision-making, but governments today are stuck in a linear, hunch-based, decision-making system. Recent technological developments mean that, for the first time, there are viable alternatives. This is being used to great effect, for example, by baseball teams today, which are running computer simulations of millions of games with and without prospective players to measure their potential impact on the team. This type of knowledge has allowed the Boston Red Sox to go from a perennial loser in the 20th century to becoming arguably the best team in major league baseball this century. Even individuals can now simulate millions of baseball games with open data and open-source software.[85]

By harnessing AI, first to aid and then increasingly to lead decision-making, the prospect arises of an Organizing System that is able to make better decisions. Freedom Age governance could run billions of simulations and scenarios and plot the complex interactions across society and the short and long-term impact of decisions, free from political or vested interests, resistance to change, and dogma. Such a governance system could help achieve the outcomes we desire, cutting through the tension that exists between short and long-term interests. Initially, this could lead towards a decentralized, network-based, direct democracy, helping citizens to take decisions by informing them of the likely impact of, for example, a new transportation bill or zoning law for cities, or of changes to energy, pollution, and rental prices. These scenarios could be run in open, transparent networks where citizens can experiment with changing assumptions and re-run simulations to learn how they apply to their families and communities. When citizens have access to the data and technology to analyze every single bill or law in the land, they may decide they do not need the Industrial Order political architecture we have today. Democracy might serve a role in choosing the outcomes we want and the principles upheld, with AI left to work out how best to achieve them.

Earth Systems

We are facing a number of critical environmental problems as the Industrial Order increasingly breaches the limits of the Earth's natural systems – greenhouse gas (GHG) emissions are rising towards thresholds that will trigger runaway climate change, forests are being cut down for fuel and agriculture, and species are being pushed to extinction, all as our cities suffocate, our rivers and waterways are polluted, and our soils are degraded. Our food system is struggling to expand in line with population growth, already harnessing as much land as is economically viable with efficiency improvements beginning to plateau, requiring ever-more inputs that run off and pollute the broader ecosystem to maintain production. Energy and resource production, likewise, is struggling to keep pace with growth, exploiting resources from increasingly difficult to reach sources while suffering from the diminishing returns of Extraction Age economics.

Just as previous civilizations have found, this is a fundamental flaw in our current system of production. The growth imperative encourages exponential growth within a finite world. This is an inherently unsustainable model – collapse is inexorable as the impact of our activities grows. The only solutions that have worked throughout history are harnessing new lands, which is impossible in a civilization with global reach and impact, or breakthrough technological improvement that allows us to do far more with far less.

The Band-Aid Solution

Our failure to understand and appreciate the emerging possibilities of the creation-based production system leads us to diagnose the wrong problem and, therefore, prescribe the wrong medicine. The climate change narrative, for example, assumes there is a cost to decarbonizing – that the emerging system is somehow more expensive than the old. According to this narrative, the solutions are behavior change and government action.

This fallacy is based on a failure to understand the processes of technology disruption. As new food, material, transport, and energy technologies outcompete Industrial Order technologies on both costs and capabilities over the next decade, the diagnosis fundamentally changes. No longer is the market a headwind acting against the emergence of the new system, but a tailwind supporting it. The challenge is not to overcome market forces but to accelerate and enable them, or at the very least to get out of their way.

The environmental narrative perceives that energy or meat consumption, for example, are 'bad'. Given this diagnosis, the solutions suggested to climate change require us to make sacrifices – to drastically reduce our energy use and meat consumption to avoid a climate tipping point – while at the same time developing technologies that pollute less. This is the inherent conflict between social and environmental outcomes in our industrial production system. A reduction in consumption on the scale required to solve climate change would lead to such economic dislocation that the capital required to develop and deploy the required technologies would not be available, locking us into our current, unsustainable system. It might buy us a few more years before we breach the thresholds that lead to runaway climate change, but breach them we will. Furthermore, the suffering involved in reducing consumption to the degree required would be unconscionable.

Moreover, the solutions currently suggested to solve these problems – behavior change, tax, and regulation – are creating political polarization and resistance, making implementation far harder. Likewise, the technological solutions to climate change suggested, like clean diesel or carbon capture and storage, are merely Band-Aids on the Industrial Order production system. Extractive technologies are already being superseded by far more robust, distributed, and cheaper technologies that utilize essentially infinite energy sources.

New Possibilities

In fact, energy, transportation, and meat consumption are not 'bad' – increases in both have delivered incredible social benefits. The externalities from them, including GHG emissions and pollution, are bad. We are fortunate that the progress of technology in our energy, transport, and agricultural sectors is driving a rapid decarbonization of our economy – driven by market forces unleashed because the emerging technologies are an order-of-magnitude superior and cheaper than the old, rather than by carbon tax, behavior change, and regulation. Solving our environmental problems will be more an outcome than a driver of technological progress.[86] The new production system will cost less – rendering the prescription of tax and subsidy redundant. Allowing this system to emerge requires the government to understand the new technologies and get out of the way, not to be in the business of energy, transportation, or food.

The land freed from agriculture offers possibilities to solve climate change that do not exist in the current food production system. As plentiful food supplies can be produced using a fraction of the landmass currently used, alternative possibilities for how we use that land emerge. Relatively low-cost reforestation at vast scale becomes viable. Furthermore, as our technological capabilities continue to improve, we should expect, within two decades, to have the capabilities to manipulate the biosphere to the extent that we can control or influence the climate system, providing that we do not pass tipping points in the meantime. We can first stop digging and then begin to fill the hole of GHG emissions.

The new, creation-based production system will operate vastly below the limits of our natural systems. Environmental problems represent a threat only if resistance to change locks us into our unsustainable Industrial-Order system. Unfortunately, our well-intentioned prescriptions risk precisely this.

Part 4

Rethinking the Future: The Path to Freedom

Rethinking the Future: The Path to Freedom

In order to solve the many problems we face in society today that if left unchecked will ultimately lead to the collapse of our civilization, and to realize the extraordinary potential of the creation-based production system, we need to enable a new Organizing System to emerge that can harness the benefits of new technologies, one that is better suited to our rapidly-changing world. But while a new system with extraordinary potential is possible, its emergence is far from inevitable. In fact, the path to get there is fraught with danger.

Resistance to Change

Our current Organizing System is deeply entrenched and reflects our most deeply-held beliefs and values, meaning resistance to fundamental change is extraordinarily strong. During our lifetimes, indeed the lifetimes of our parents and grandparents, the system has been a constant, so the idea that the concepts underpinning it like modern democracy, nation states, capitalism, or individual rights could change radically seems inconceivable.

Figure 13. **Surfing the Tsunami: Factors Driving Societal Breakthrough or Collapse**

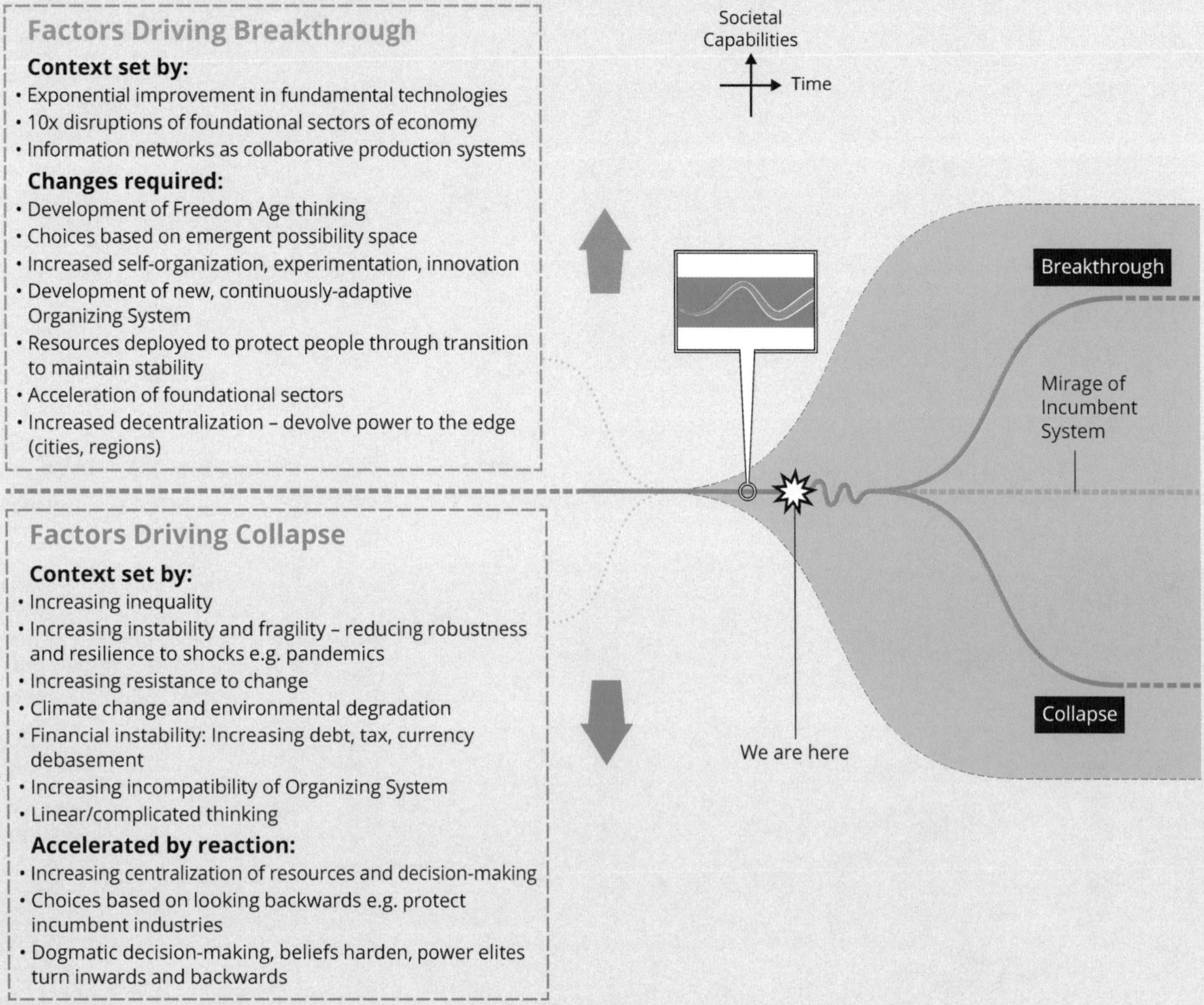

Factors Driving Breakthrough

Context set by:
- Exponential improvement in fundamental technologies
- 10x disruptions of foundational sectors of economy
- Information networks as collaborative production systems

Changes required:
- Development of Freedom Age thinking
- Choices based on emergent possibility space
- Increased self-organization, experimentation, innovation
- Development of new, continuously-adaptive Organizing System
- Resources deployed to protect people through transition to maintain stability
- Acceleration of foundational sectors
- Increased decentralization – devolve power to the edge (cities, regions)

Factors Driving Collapse

Context set by:
- Increasing inequality
- Increasing instability and fragility – reducing robustness and resilience to shocks e.g. pandemics
- Increasing resistance to change
- Climate change and environmental degradation
- Financial instability: Increasing debt, tax, currency debasement
- Increasing incompatibility of Organizing System
- Linear/complicated thinking

Accelerated by reaction:
- Increasing centralization of resources and decision-making
- Choices based on looking backwards e.g. protect incumbent industries
- Dogmatic decision-making, beliefs harden, power elites turn inwards and backwards

Societal Capabilities
Time
Breakthrough
Mirage of Incumbent System
Collapse
We are here

Source: RethinkX

When threatened with disruption, civilizations (just like companies) are incapable of taking the short-term pain required to make the changes necessary for longer-term survival until it is too late. Indeed an immune response causes incumbents to crush the early shoots of disruption before they can blossom. They focus their efforts and discussions instead on patching up the existing system with a minor tweak here or there – inadequate and misguided solutions to a far deeper problem.

But history teaches us that Organizing Systems are variables, not constants. They do change fundamentally and when they change, they change fast as the civilizations they underpin collapse. Every leading civilization has followed this path to implosion. During periods of instability, as civilizations reach their limits and begin to fall, populations seek comfort in certainty and crave the status quo, reducing the system's flexibility and making change harder to effect. **Just at the point when our decision-making processes and Organizing System need to adapt fundamentally, they become increasingly inflexible and resistant to change.**

Ultimately, the increasing inflexibility of our Organizing System will only hasten its demise. **The only hope is that a new system that allows us to capture the extraordinary benefits of technological progress emerges in advance of collapse.**

History indicates we face two possible outcomes:

1. **Breakthrough.** A new Organizing System emerges that can make sense of, and manage effectively, the emerging production system, allowing us to break through to a higher order.[87]

2. **Collapse.** We follow the course of all previous civilizations and collapse back to a lower order as we fail to escape the constraints of the industrial Organizing System.

Breakthrough

Societal breakthroughs to a higher order have never been planned. They have emerged through endless experimentation and iterations across cultures and geographies until a state accidentally stumbled across the right fit of production and Organizing Systems. These societies, from Mesopotamia and Egypt to Rome and the UK, came from the edge of the previous civilizations and emerged after hundreds of years of dark ages.

They were all 'start-up' states that developed new Organizing Systems that fitted both the production system of their times and their geographical endowment, triggering the development of new societal capabilities. Similarly, the next world order leader will be the one that can develop new models of thought that adequately explain the world today and encourage an Organizing System that fits the emerging production system. This model will then accelerate technological progress, outcompete our existing Industrial Organizing System and spread as it is copied, pasted, and adapted.

Benevolent or Dystopian? It Depends...

Societal breakthroughs can be benevolent or dystopian, depending on your vantage point. The rise of Europe after 1500 was clearly dystopian for Native Americans, Africans, and Asian societies.

Slavery is one dimension of this dystopia. While ancient Athens developed axial thought, perhaps as many as two thirds of the ancient Athenian population was enslaved.[88] Rome enslaved as much as a third of its population. As recently as 1800, roughly three-quarters of the world's population may have lived in bondage.[89] To build a socially complex society at the center, not only did civilizations exploit people and resources at the periphery, but they brought war, deforestation, soil exhaustion and salinization, and disease.

Benevolent Breakthrough

If we can develop a new Organizing System that is designed to benefit humanity, not any single individual or group of individuals, we will create some incredible possibilities over the 2020s and into the 2030s.

Poverty could cease to exist as the new system of production can fulfil our basic needs at near zero cost. The cost of the American Dream, thought of in terms of 1,000 miles/month of transport, 2,000 kWh/month of energy, complete nutrition (including 100 grams of protein, 250 grams of healthy carbs, 70 grams of fats, and micronutrients), 100 liters of clean water a day, continuing education, 500 sq. ft. of living space, and communications, could be less than $250/month by 2030 and half that by 2035.[90] A new social contract that provides a minimum quality of life encompassing these basic needs becomes possible, not just in America but throughout the world.

Geography, historically a key determinant of competitive advantage, will be increasingly less important, with communities everywhere able to access locally the key building blocks of their economies to become self-sufficient in food, energy, transportation, information, and materials.

Prosperous, livable cities of 100 million people or more will become viable. As the limitations in energy, transportation, and communication technologies that have given rise to cluster effects for cities diminish and demands on land from our industrial food system reduce, networked, distributed communities of almost limitless scale become possible, almost entirely autonomous in systems of governance and production.

Localized bonds of kinship and the need for scale that necessitated and underpinned nation states will be replaced by bonds of kinship that act in multiple dimensions, rendering our most fundamental centralized governance structures obsolete. Digital-first institutions, communities, and bonds of kinship will replace the industrial, tribal kinship model.

Distributed trust based on accessible, immutable, verifiable transactions and other personal and business history will undermine the value of brands and usurp even governments as the intermediaries of trust. Technologies such as blockchain, for example, have the potential to disintermediate some of the core institutions of the industrial Organizing System, such as commercial and central banks, and political parties. It could also enable new concepts such as triple-entry accounting which would help us achieve new levels of institutional trust by allowing all parties in the network (consumers, creators, producers, voters, and individual investors) to have access to complete transaction records, not just the curated summaries that centralized institutions and auditors disclose today. Dismissing blockchain's potential to disintermediate legacy institutions and help enable new types of institutional trust would be the modern equivalent of dismissing music streaming or social media because Napster and Friendster failed.

Low-cost plenitude will make extraction and exploitation obsolete. As everyone is freed from indigence, precarity, and violence, society will no longer need to tolerate inequality. Economic elites, if they exist, will find they can produce nearly everything without the need to exploit humans or nature. The age-old, winner-takes-all extraction strategy of pitting groups against one another will disappear.

The networked system will be far more robust and resilient. More capable of experimenting and adapting to shocks, millions of self-sufficient, self-governing nodes will replace a few dozen centralized nation states, providing a vast increase in both diversity and quality of decision-making. As the need for scale and reach diminishes along with the flow of physical goods, and perhaps people, resilience will grow and supply-chain security will improve dramatically.

Geopolitical tensions should diminish over the longer term in a world where control of scarce resources is far less important. Indeed the underlying causes of conflict, rooted in the winner-takes-all imperative of extraction economics, will dramatically diminish or disappear. Trillion-dollar military expenditures on traditional planes, ships, missiles, and guns will be replaced by new forms of remote, digitalized warfare.

Climate change and environmental degradation, caused by a system that drives endless growth within a finite system and ignores externalities, will be overcome by market forces that deliver superior, cheaper, and more convenient sources of food, transport, energy, and materials that produce close to zero CO_2 emissions and have little impact on our ecosystems. Furthermore, increased technological capability will allow us to reverse much of the catastrophic environmental damage we have created.

In an era where we can manipulate matter, energy, and information from a quantum level to a planetary scale with order-of-magnitude improvements in cost, speed, and precision, where the building blocks of the production system are available and plentiful everywhere at essentially zero cost, the capability frontier of what is possible may well be the laws of physics. The effect on every aspect of society will be extraordinary, opening up the possibility of a society that escapes the growth imperative and operates indefinitely within the Earth's limits.

Framework Box 8. The Possibility Space: Exploding Opportunities

Convergence opens up new possibilities. At a sector level, the convergence of technologies creates new possibilities not only for new products and services but for new business models and value chains. More than that, it creates possibilities across other sectors of the economy and society more broadly. At the level of a civilization, the same dynamic occurs as production and Organizing System convergence expands the possibilities of what a civilization is capable of. These future possibilities can be seen as the possibility space.

Technological progress removes constraints on what we can do and achieve and creates entirely new possibilities in how we live our lives and meet our needs – in a very real sense, it represents humanity's journey from the impossible to the possible. The scope of what is possible can be seen as the emergent possibility space of our civilization. Huge strides have been made by the technology we have already invented, but our current technologies are far from perfect and we are nowhere near the capability frontier represented by the laws of physics. In the Age of Freedom, progress could trend towards this potential.

The possibility space encompasses breakthrough on the upside and collapse on the downside. There is a high probability that the outcome falls in either of these two extremes, with almost zero probability of an intermediate outcome, which represents an indefinite continuation of our current civilization.

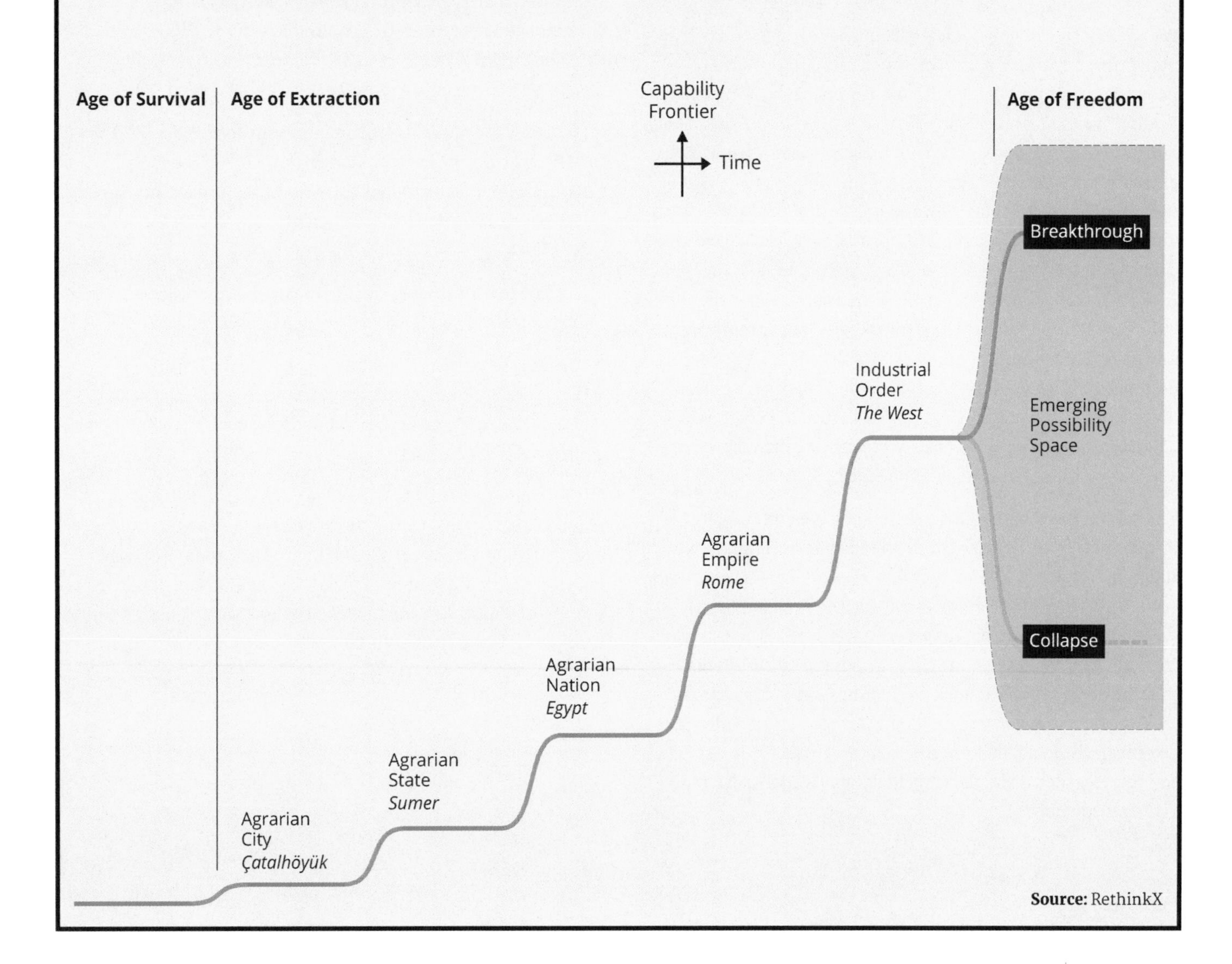

Source: RethinkX

Dystopian Breakthrough

If a new Organizing System does emerge in time, there is no guarantee it will deliver this prosperous, fair, and stable world if ownership structures are not completely rethought.

Civilizations in the Age of Extraction required widespread support from, or control of, those it exploited. The Organizing System created the push and pull that influenced, harnessed, and controlled the actions of millions of people. As a new system emerges, freed from reliance on humans for labor and innovation, and with potentially an unprecedented disparity in capabilities between those who control the system and those who do not, the need for support will drop away.[91] With little need to incentivize participation and support, the possibility arises of a system controlled and exploited by a small, all-powerful group and not managed in the interest of humanity. A dystopia.

We already have technological capabilities to destroy the planet many times over, but given the exponential improvement in our ability to manipulate matter, energy, and information, leading societies of the future will have an order-of-magnitude more destructive power. The technologies that create such extraordinary possibilities will also empower small groups or individuals to wreak havoc on society. Picture pandemics with viruses designed by individuals specifically to cause maximum damage, weather-modification warfare technologies, pocket rockets carrying nuclear weapons aimed at our water supply, automated mass quantum hacking of personal, commercial, and government bank accounts, and a new technologically-enhanced, 'superior' human species. None of these scenarios are science fiction – the technologies that would give rise to them are either here or possible with improvements in costs and capabilities of existing technologies.

The state created and subsidized the internet and the GPS system until they became commercially viable. Should a few individuals hack their way to trillion-dollar gains by extracting from the very population that invested their tax dollars in developing the network? Taxpayers have similarly subsidized technologies that are on the cusp of opening up enormous possibilities for society, such as quantum computing and AI. Holding on to our current ownership structures (including IP regimes) within a new Organizing System would give rise to precisely such a prospect and inevitably lead to a dramatic rise in inequality.

Collapse

The alternative is a breakdown of the current system as the world descends into a new dark age, capable of supporting only a fraction of the current population. In line with previous collapses, the complex causes of this breakdown might include climate change, famine, social unrest driven by increasing inequality, disease, or a multitude of other inter-related causes leading to increasing warfare or state failure. Underpinning them all, however, is a civilization that has reached its limits and an Organizing System that can no longer adapt to the pace of change.

Transitioning to the Future

Never before have we had the potential to break through the capability frontier of a civilization in advance of its collapse. **Humanity, therefore, is in a unique position – for the first time in history, we have the opportunity to enable the emergence of a new Organizing System without first descending into a dark age.** In order to succeed, we must overcome a three-fold challenge:

1. **Rethink** the present and the future: To appreciate what is happening in the world today and develop the tools to understand and manage the emerging Organizing System in a way that is beyond our current Industrial Order models of thought.
2. **Enable** the future we want: To create the conditions in which this new system can emerge and flourish.
3. **Bridge** the journey: To manage the transition while somehow keeping our current system functioning in the face of unprecedented change long enough for a new system to emerge.

The emergent nature of change means that, while the magnitude, speed, and direction of change are apparent, the exact attributes of a new Organizing System are unknowable today. So while we cannot plan this system, we can plan the process and mechanisms to guide and enable it to emerge through trial and (painful) error.

Understanding the Age of Freedom

The linear, reductionist, deterministic models of thought that have helped drive extraordinary progress through the Industrial Order are increasingly less able to comprehend our world, just as those rooted in the religious dogma of the medieval world were unable to explain and manage the emerging industrial world. Our existing models break down the enormous complexity of reality into manageable parts but ignore the whole, just as medicine has fractured into different specialties but lost focus on the inter-relationships between them. They focus on linear cause and effect, meaning they treat symptoms and then symptoms of side effects. They fail to understand the complexity that would allow us to identify root causes and optimize the whole.

This reductionism is reflected in the silos that have developed in education, science, academia, government, industry, and in the increasing specialization of labor, as the complexity of the whole is broken down into individual parts, disciplines, departments, or jobs. This blinded us to many of the non-linear outcomes of our actions. Implicit in our models of thought has been a determinism that suggests outcomes can be predetermined from starting conditions - this change causes that effect, but "all else remains equal" (et ceteris paribus). This way of thinking ignores emergence and the second-order effects that occur in all complex systems.

This deep, segmented knowledge is hugely valuable and must not be discarded, but to thrive in the coming age we will need to find ways to reassemble these fragmented parts and understand the system as a whole, with all its complexity. In many ways, our Industrial Order could be best understood by the rules of classical physics and linear causality, but the models of thought required in the Age of Freedom will mirror biology and systems dynamics.

As writer and thinker Emilios Bouratinos has said: "The universe is not a gigantic clockwork orange. It is a living, self-organizing system that changes even its mechanism of change from one level of complexification to the next." [92]

The belief in individual rights which is a foundation block of our Industrial Order has served a purpose, with millions of individuals acting in their own interests, approximating the best outcome for the whole. But reality is different. We now understand how interconnected we are, impacting each other through our thoughts, ideas, words, energy, and actions. The determinism, centralization, and uniformity reflected in our economic, political, and social systems add to the fragility of our society, leading to a herd effect in decision-making. Mirroring the self-organizing rules of biological systems will increase our resilience and allow us to prioritize the benefit of the network (whole) over the individual.

The new ways of thinking that better explain the world around us, the metrics and processes to manage this world, and the belief systems that will underpin it are, as yet, unclear. The work of Socrates, Aristotle, Plato, Buddha, Jesus, and Confucius helped shape early civilizations, while the reason of Newton, Galileo, Descartes, Bacon, Locke, Adam Smith, and myriad others helped enable the Industrial Order. We do not yet know who their equivalents will be. They are likely to emerge from the disciplines of biology, complexity, and network and systems theory. The ancient Eastern philosophies that stress the interconnectedness of everything, the need to see the world as it is and to embrace change, might be seeds that can germinate in the emergent belief systems.

Rethinking the Present and the Future

The first step is to see the speed, magnitude, and non-linear nature of the emergence of the production system to come. Linear thinking is not just unhelpful but dangerous, as it leads us to think that change will be slow, controllable, and require minor adaptations to the existing production and Organizing Systems. The breakthrough possibility space, which represents the full potential for human thriving, remains hidden from view.

Even exponential thinking, while more accurate than linear in understanding the technological potential, ignores the need for Organizing Systems. As we have seen, history clearly shows us technology alone will not lead to a breakthrough in societal capabilities – we need the right Organizing Systems to capture the possibilities that technological development opens up.

We can guide and even accelerate the adaptation process by anticipating the speed and scale of change and by understanding the attributes of the new system so we can create the right conditions for it to emerge. We can only do this by having more accurate expectations of what the future holds.

We will need to rethink the very concepts that underpin our Organizing System, concepts that represent some of our most deeply-held beliefs, including democracy, belief in individual rights, nation states, free-market capitalism, and our social contract. We will need to develop new models of thought and conceptual frameworks that can better understand and explain both the world today and what is coming. Supplementing the linear, reductionist thought models of the Industrial Order with an understanding of complex causality across systems will be key – the understanding of physics (extraction) supplemented by biology (creation) and applied to human systems.

With this understanding, we can begin to appreciate the attributes and drivers of the emerging Organizing System. Recognizing the incompatibility of our governance, social, economic, and political systems might help reduce our attachment to them and quash the immune response, allowing us to create the conditions for a new Organizing System to emerge. Not only will all these systems need re-imagining, but we might need to question our very concept of humanity. How our basic needs for survival and 'growth' manifest in this new world is uncertain, but our consciousness and the behaviors we consider innate will shift, driving the formation of new belief systems and values. The rights of the individual might even be replaced by the rights of the network or community.

Enabling the Future we Want

The transition will be neither smooth nor planned centrally by any leading country. They are poorly positioned precisely because they have become so successful. The immune response is too strong. The U.S., Europe, or China, therefore, are unlikely to lead the way. In a globally-competitive world, smaller, hungrier, more adaptable communities, cities, or states, such as Israel, Mumbai, Dubai, Singapore, Lagos, Shanghai, California, or Seattle, are more likely to develop the winning Organizing System. They will appear, just like their predecessors, as if from nowhere, with capabilities far beyond those of existing leaders. History indicates the new system will spread through imitation (best case) or force (worst case). For example, the Mumbai Western Europe Company could be in a position to overwhelm Europe like the British EIC once dominated India, the Batavia Netcorp could remotely raid Dutch banks like the VOC once raided Indonesian islands, or the Moscow NetLC[93] could design a new virus, inoculate its own population and then unleash a viral pandemic on the U.S. or UK.

Will China Lead in the Age of Freedom?

After becoming the world leader in packetizing materials, China has moved to become the world leader in packetizing information. It has emerged as the new leader in next generation (5G) communication technologies, shocking politicians and mainstream commentators who are calling for Extraction Age tools (trade sanctions, military action, and xenophobia) to manage this development. China has also become the world leader in Freedom Age transportation (on-demand, autonomous and EVs) and energy (solar, wind, and batteries) production systems. Washington's response, meanwhile, has been predictable - subsidize and protect the legacy fossil fuel industry and electric power monopolies.

China is thus leading, or is within striking distance of, the U.S. in four of the five foundational sectors that are driving the emergence the new age. But this does not mean it is destined to lead in the Age of Freedom. Just like any other leading country today or civilization throughout history, China will need to allow a new Organizing System to emerge, which involves a willingness not just to rethink its mechanisms for governance and its most deeply-held beliefs, but to overcome incumbency at every level. Will China, with its centralized, command and control structure, be willing to devolve power to the edge?

History indicates that self-organization, networks, and openness to new ideas, innovation, and people will be key to break through. For instance, open immigration has been essential to previous leading civilizations. The U.S. had open immigration until it emerged as the world's leading power in the 1920s. Between 1900 and 1914, more than 13 million immigrants arrived in the U.S. and by the end of the period 60% of industrial workers were born abroad.[94] The industries that gave birth to the American Century could not have been built without immigrants. Silicon Valley, which is leading the development of the emerging system of production, is no different today – 68% of Silicon Valley tech workers (aged between 25-44) are foreign born.[95] To lead the next world order, Silicon Valley, Seattle, or Boston would have to have its own immigration powers.

This would require the centers of power to give up control – something that is antithetical to the very fabric of nation-state governments.[96] How much control will the center allow their regions with no guarantee of success? China, for example, would have to allow several regions to experiment until one of them emerged with breakthrough capabilities, with other regions then copy and pasting the winning combination.

To overcome the power of incumbency, our mindsets must evolve to embrace change rather than fear it, to challenge pre-conceptions and rethink everything from first principles. We must resist incumbency at every level, from the influence of powerful groups to our dependency on current systems, concepts, and beliefs.

This process will be like surfing a tsunami. Principles like experimentation, iteration, and a willingness to fail and learn will be critical. The emerging, networked system will be far more conducive to trial and error than the centralized, interdependent structure of the Industrial Order. Flexibility and adaptability will need to be built into every facet of society. Networked communities or regions could run thousands of self-organized experiments and constantly monitor outcomes if the center stepped back and resisted the temptation to interfere or crush them as they began to threaten the existing system.

The emerging Organizing System will need to decentralize decision-making to communities and cities while finding ways to make meaningful decisions at a network level for issues that might require global management, such as control of technologies like AI and quantum computing, human population, pandemic response, shared resources (water, air, and forests), or climate control. Governance of the network might require a modern-day Philadelphia Convention to set out the principles of the new system and the priorities to optimize for.

Bridging the Journey

As well as laying the foundations for a new Organizing System to emerge, we will need to keep our current system functioning during the transition in order to deliver the continued technological progress necessary to underpin the new system. Finding ways to create enough resilience to allow the transition to continue will be critical. Some of the Band-Aids on the industrial system will have a role in this process but should not be mistaken for credible, long-term solutions.

The transition will be hard, amounting perhaps to little more than organized chaos, but a strong vision of where we are heading and a clear explanation of why we must get there might help create the support needed to stay on track.

But left, right, and center must recognize that their world views are increasingly obsolete. We need to walk a delicate tightrope over the next decade – keeping social stability, cohesion, and trust without tempering the creative forces that drive innovation and progress. Pressure to move towards extremes will increase if we fail to understand what is happening, with an increase in resistance to change from incumbent mindsets, beliefs, behaviors, and interest groups. When the new system emerges, this tension will disappear.

One of biggest risks during the transition will be military conflict, as war has been part of the collapse of every leading civilization in history. As tensions rise, incumbent interest groups will weaponize uncertainty and inflame fear of 'the other' (both inside and out) to instigate conflict. Information warfare has always been used in the Extraction Age, with false narratives, fake news, and pseudo facts creating and inflaming the demand for war. The difference today is that anyone, anywhere can employ this arsenal cheaply through social media with few or no consequences for themselves. This erodes trust and increases instability in the system.

States and regions that are reliant on the resource intensity of the current extractive production system, such as the Middle East and Russia, could be the first to break down. A drop in the cost of export commodities would cause a decline in government revenues, and thus a disproportionate cut in social spending and a rise in debts, both of which would make the system even more unstable. There will be calls for increased funding for conventional military warfare, even though they are increasingly obsolete in the age of cyber warfare, leading to a disproportionate increase in military expenditures as a percentage of government income. All these destabilizing forces will push these societies towards disintegration with disturbing possibilities, such as an increase in suppression and violence followed by civil unrest and chaos.

Choices

Maintaining system stability during this turbulent period will, therefore, be a huge challenge, a challenge that no previous leading civilization has overcome when faced with collapse. Whether we can break the pattern of history depends on the choices we make today.

We can choose to be fearful of losing what we have and fight to defend it, but this is a battle we will undoubtedly lose. The collapse of the existing, extraction-based system has already started and is inevitable. Clinging to the principles and beliefs that underpin it, seeing them as immutable constants for all time rather than the man-made, ephemeral constructs they are, will simply accelerate this collapse.

Or we can choose to create an extraordinary future for humanity, a future where poverty no longer exists and every one of us has the fundamental right to all our basic needs. A future where we can all live and thrive well within the biophysical limits of the Earth, free from the existential threat of human-made climate change. A future where we can, for the first time in history, achieve true freedom.

The first step towards doing so is to remove the blindfold of our linear, mechanistic, and siloed mindset. Equipped with a new understanding and a framework that captures the complexity of our civilization, we can understand the problems we face today in a new light and recognize and more accurately foresee the extraordinary potential opening up ahead of us.

Only by recognizing the range of possibilities, both good and bad, can we hope to reach our potential. In some ways, just a recognition of an alternative future can become self-fulfilling. In a globally competitive world, those regions that are best able to harness a more suitable Organizing System will thrive and dominate, while those that cling to the past will be left behind. Resistance to change, inertia, or indifference are not an option. They are the path to destruction.

Which road we take depends on our choices. We have an incredible opportunity to embrace technological progress and create a new Organizing System to help build a healthier, fairer, more prosperous, and resilient world for every one of us. We must take it.

RethinkX 2020–2030 Action Plan

As successive, predictable shocks destabilize our civilization, the knee-jerk response of greater centralization in decision-making and resource allocation will give nation states, previously gridlocked by polarization, the power and the ability to take decisive action. It is imperative that this power is not used to prop up the old system but to accelerate the new.

Here is some high-level guidance together with specific examples of interventions that governments, investors, and businesses can make to delay the collapse of our industrial system and accelerate breakthrough of the new creation-based production system.

High Level

- **Recognize where we are** and the threats to our system. There is no going back, no return to 'normal'. We are at a rupture point and the old rules no longer apply. Actions taken in a stable system can have the opposite effect when the system is out of equilibrium.
- **Be prepared for regular shocks** throughout the 2020s. Examples include financial and real estate crises, pandemics, social unrest, state failure, environmental catastrophes, and mass migration. They will compound the destabilization caused by the rapid transformation of our production system brought about by technological disruption to every sector of the economy.
- **Pay attention to the cascading impacts of sector disruptions.** Every major sector of the economy will be disrupted during the 2020s. The implications of these disruptions for other sectors will be just as impactful as the initial disruptions themselves. For example, the disruption of transportation (see *Rethinking Transportation 2020–2030*) will drive the market price of oil down to around $25 as soon as 2021, which will cause whole segments of the oil industry to collapse (including oil sands, deepwater oil, and shale/tight oil) with knock-on effects across their value chains (refineries, pipelines, shipping, engineering, construction, and steel). Since oil is the largest tradable commodity in the world, credit markets will be hit as the industry is unable to service its debt, or even goes bankrupt. Since oil is tied to the dollar, the world's reserve currency's hegemony will be undermined, with potential implications for interest rates (which affect, for example, real estate, construction, concrete, and car sales) and U.S. geopolitical power. Equally, the disruption of transportation will also drive the resale value of ICE cars, trucks, buses, and vans down to zero or even negative territory.[97] A single percentage point decline in resale value could cost car manufacturers hundreds of millions of dollars. A collapse in resale value could cause liquidity problems, which again would have implications for jobs and credit markets. Likewise, disruption to information and communications could dramatically reduce the need for physical presence and hence transportation, which will be further impacted by the order-of-magnitude drop in shipping goods and resources (oil, coal, cars, and food), with knock-on effects for roads, trucks, rail, and shipping.
- **Balance the need for rapid change with measures to increase social, economic, and political stability** (see below). This will be a critical challenge.
- **Create a vision and a clear plan** to mitigate adverse outcomes, such as job losses, instability, and uncertainty.
- **Communicate them clearly** in order to create broad social support.
- **Realize that this is a race to the top.** Those that get left behind will be trapped in the legacy industrial system as it enters a death spiral of decreasing demand and investment and increasing costs. Those that lead will be in a position to set the new global rules of engagement.
- **Devolve power to cities, regions, and states.** Encourage self-organization, management of local production, and flexibility in planning, investing, and governance.
- **Value robustness and resiliency.** For example, one hundred million homes, commercial buildings, warehouses, and factories generating and storing electric energy is a far more robust and resilient system than a few power plants and a centralized, 20th century grid. Equally, distributed, local food production through PF is far more robust and resilient than a centralized system that fails to deliver food during times of crisis. Robustness and resilience must be priced in when building new infrastructure.
- **Rethink old concepts like efficiency and economies of scale,** which come at the price of vulnerability and single points of failure. Just as the internet created an information network that has proved capable of withstanding and absorbing shocks (such as Covid-19), the creation-based production system architecture will enable local production, storage, and distribution that are impervious to shocks. For essential needs such as food, energy, and transportation, aim for robust and resilient, local self-sufficiency, not vulnerable, just-in-time, global supply chains.
- **Recognize that we already have the tools we need.** We need no technological breakthroughs. This is largely about execution, and hence capital investments. Scale-up will deliver predictable and exponential improvements in costs and capabilities over time as the new system rapidly outcompetes the old, meaning that market forces will be a tailwind and not the headwind predicted by mainstream analysis.

- **Do not give credence to incumbents' linear forecasts** that fail to account for the complexity that drives non-linear improvements in cost and adoption of new technologies. Incumbent industries, captured government agencies, and the mainstream analysts they consult have different incentives to the rest of society. Before putting taxpayer, ratepayer, or pension money at risk, take the time to assess mainstream forecasters' predictions from 10 or 15 years ago versus the reality today. Hold them accountable for their predictions, which have been wrong and continue to be wrong by orders of magnitude.

Accelerate the New System of Production

Governments should focus on accelerating the roll-out of new infrastructure and value chains in the foundational sectors – information, energy, transportation, food, and materials. Other sectors will benefit greatly from these investments. In tandem, governments must stop investing in building new capacity in old infrastructure, which will result in the lock-in of uncompetitive systems, stranded assets, and trillions of dollars of losses. The focus should be on:

Information: 5G, broadband, small satellite networks, UAV, and other forms of modern information networks.

Energy: Solar, wind, and batteries.

Transport: Batteries, fleet-charging networks, support for AVs/micro-mobility, and integration and conversion of rail and public transit with TaaS.

Food: Distributed, localized, PF production hubs.

Materials: Building production capacity for organic materials through PF. These modern materials will help accelerate roll-out across the other foundational sectors.

The Rules

Create frameworks to incentivize the scale-up of the new system through rules and regulation, legislation, law, tax, subsidy regimes, and investment incentives.

- **Governments should prioritize deployment of existing foundational sector technologies, not basic research and development.** We already have the technologies that will disrupt food, energy, and transportation. Government investment in R&D in these technologies brought them to this point but businesses can and should make the necessary investments to push solar PV, batteries, EVs, AVs, and PF to economic viability and disruption of legacy industries. Government support should focus on removing obstacles that stand in the way of widespread deployment.
- **Governments should enable well-regulated markets but should not participate in or distort industries.** For example, today the U.S. government stockpiles 1.4 billion pounds of cheese that it pushes in the form of school lunches and the Supplemental Nutrition Assistance Program.
  - **Governments should exit the energy business** – they should not own electric power generation, transmission, pipelines, and mines.
- **Remove barriers to the new system, including unnecessary red tape, regulations, and laws.** For example, end onerous municipal, state, or federal requirements for distributed solar installations. Users must be connected within 24 hours of building a distributed solar/battery installation. In urban planning, end minimum parking requirements (off and on-street), exclusionary zoning laws, onerous housing density requirements, requirements for converting existing parking and garage space to housing, office, and shops, and be ready to close unnecessary streets and plan for their redevelopment into parks, higher-density housing, affordable housing, businesses, on-demand workspace, and mobile retail.
- **Stop all subsidies (direct and indirect) to legacy sectors.**
- **Remove regulatory support for legacy systems.** For example, gas connectivity should not be required for new residential and commercial buildings. Parking requirements should not be required for new-build residential or commercial projects. Allow builders to build parking according to consumer needs, not government requirements.
- **Design open, fair, transparent, and competitive markets** that remove barriers to new entrants and reduce the ability for monopolies to form. For example, grant the right to individuals and businesses to produce, store, and trade electricity. Remove restrictions on decentralized power generation.
- **Create universal standards for new product approval, connectivity, and access.** For example, provide easy, instant connectivity to the new electricity grid (resembling how internet service providers can join the net without needing permission from the center). Create open platforms and standards for the provision of TaaS. Create standards and remove barriers for EV connectivity to the grid (V2G).
  - Update and streamline evaluation processes using computer simulation. For example, to understand the impact of food products and their ingredients on human health.

- **Use tax and subsidy to accelerate the transition.** For example, accelerated depreciation allowances on new infrastructure.
  - Price negative externalities by taxing the most damaging and unhealthy products to reflect their broader costs to society, including zoonotic viruses.
- **Use regulations to support the new system.** For example, as a minimum, require all new buildings in urban areas to be electric-only (i.e. no gas or petrol allowed for space heating or even cooking). Better still, require all new buildings to have solar, battery storage, and electric V2G connections, and the ability to add more solar and batteries like Lego. Require all roof replacement projects to include solar generation.
  - Establish independent regulatory bodies where necessary. For example, to develop policies and oversee modern food technologies and their products, especially given the lobbying power of the conventional food industry and potential conflicts of interest between the old and new industries.
- **Accelerate scale-up of the new system** through direct investment and investment incentives. For example, fast track development of AV technology.
- **Set and signal clear intentions to provide clarity and certainty** to investors, businesses, and consumers through targets for adoption of new technologies and restrictions on old. For example, signpost a ban on gasoline or diesel vehicle sales from 2025 and the use of such vehicles from 2030. Signal plans to ban diesel generators in urban and suburban areas by 2025. Provide incentives to swap old diesel generators for battery storage ('battery storage for clunkers').
- **Adapt metrics and taxation to fit the new system.** For example, for transportation, move taxes and fees for TaaS to a cents-per-mile basis to replace gasoline tax and annual vehicle fees. Keep gasoline taxes for ICE vehicles as the industry winds down. Do not tax solar self-generation or energy storage, only tax sales to the grid or third parties.
- **Adapt subsidies to fit the new system.** For transportation, consider a zero-emission-miles (ZEM) not zero-emissions-vehicle (ZEV) incentive. Incentives for purchasing vehicles (ZEV) encourage inefficient use of more vehicles that impose up to 10x more costs on society through inefficient resource utilization and externalizing costs (for example materials, traffic, and parking space needs).[98]
- **Support the creation of open-source, transparent, collaborative networks** – preferably international – to accelerate the pace of development.
- **Develop new models for community ownership of platforms and networks** (energy, information, and transportation). Private ownership and competition should be focused on ideas (information) and elements of the value chain that sit on top of the networks and platform (e.g. production, distribution, and retail).
- **Adapt intellectual property (IP) regimes.** IP rights that are in place to create incentives for investment in certain sectors can also limit technological progress and create unnecessary costs to consumers. For example, imposing a pharmaceutical-style IP regime on food would increase costs dramatically, slow the development of the market, and prevent an open-source food production system from emerging. Time-limited IP rights should be granted only when in the public interest, where investment in development would not otherwise happen.
  - Allow companies to patent production methods but not biological entities, life, or genes – IP regimes should be process-focused rather than output-focused. This will encourage innovators to adopt and develop the technology and encourage the development of open-source platforms and molecular, cellular, and biological system databases.
- **Give individuals control and ownership of data rights.** Information is at the center of each disruption – consumer data on energy use, transport, personalized nutrition, and healthcare, for example, have value. Ensuring individual ownership and control of private data will provide economic benefits to consumers that are currently being extracted by third parties. It will also provide benefits like privacy and security. Treating user data like IP should be considered – individuals would own all personal data and have the right to license it to anyone on their own terms. That is, 'legal agreements,' whereby companies like Facebook, Google, and Amazon, compel users to give up rights to their data in exchange for access to apps, should be illegal. Just like IP licensing agreements, individuals should have the right to license data on a per-use, time-limited basis. They should also be able to exclude usage. Companies should bid for the right to use individual data like they bid for people's labor. Individuals should have the right to offer their data and IP under terms they find favorable.
- **Create rules to ensure open access to data and interfaces when in the public interest.** For example, 3D High Definition mapping and traffic flow data for transportation of energy, goods, and people should be openly accessible.

- **Design energy, transport, and production networks based on scale-free network design.** For example, transition the centralized, one-way electric power grid to a networked, multi-way grid. This is like the transition of the centralized, one-way newspaper, radio, or broadcast TV information flow to an internet-based model where everyone can generate, store, and share or trade content. Aim for an energy network that resembles the internet.
- **Build adaptability into infrastructure.** For example, ensure that new-build solar, wind, and battery capacity built around the centralized electric power grid is adaptable to the fully decentralized energy system that will emerge. Equally, encourage standards to ensure that a charging network for privately-owned electric vehicles is ready for the emergence of shared autonomous fleets.
- **Regulatory requirements should aim for flexible, distributed, localized, robust production networks.** For example, road use should be flexible, so that both lanes and parking can be assigned to the most appropriate use (e.g. bicycles, scooters, delivery robots, robo-taxis, and high-occupancy vehicles) in real time. Plan for road usage fees to be based on social goals as well as the cost of infrastructure – for example, tax empty vehicle miles, congested road usage, and heavier vehicles at a higher rate than high-occupancy (e.g. buses) and light vehicles (e.g. bikes and scooters). Plan for flexibility in pricing and integrating real-time pricing information into mapping software so that vehicles can optimize driving routes in real time. Plan for the impact of disruptions on related sectors – for example integrating TaaS fleets with transit, rail, and micro-mobility solutions.
- **Balance safety with the need for rapid transition in regulatory-approval processes.** There is inevitably conflict between approving new technologies (e.g. AVs or PF foods) and public safety. Regulatory approval processes can impose costs and delays on new technologies. Decisions here need careful consideration of the full costs and wider benefits of transition, not a narrow focus on direct impacts. Many barriers to adoption can be removed without any trade off.
- **Use rules around insurance to accelerate the transition.** For example, no-fault insurance for AV technology would mean that insurers pay the injured party regardless of fault, where the owner of the vehicle is the insured party. In other words, use the same insurance system for human and autonomous drivers. Resist the pressure to subsidize human-driven vehicles when it becomes clear they are measurably more dangerous than autonomous vehicles.
  - Allow transportation companies to self-insure. This will provide incentives for them to develop safer transportation technology.
  - Governments should not insure outdated legacy systems, such as fossil fuel or nuclear energy projects.
- **Governments should be aware of the role they can play in shaping public opinion** and resisting the inevitable push back from incumbent interests that are at risk from disruption.
  - **Increase transparency.** For example, modernize food labeling to better communicate health benefits, health risks, and environmental impacts to consumers. Labeling laws should have clear meanings. The word 'natural,' for example, does not have a clear legal meaning today and can be used by food marketers to mislead consumers. Establish clear, official terms and definitions in conjunction with the food industry, both legacy and new, that government agencies use when referring to various products and their production methods that do not favor one industry over another.
  - **Prioritize consumers' right to know.** Instead of simplistic, static food labels, for example, consumers should be able to scan a QR code that shows details of the content of food they intend to purchase, including the source of all ingredients, manufacturing methods, heavy metal content, health impact to children and adults, and environmental impact. Data should include names of companies and GPS location of farms and factories for all ingredients, all of which are available in disparate databases today.
  - Create standards for users to download food data to nutrition apps so they and their nutritionists can optimize individual health outcomes.
- **Governments should lead by example in their own procurement programs.** For example, all government buildings should install solar and battery storage. Transportation, governments, public transportation agencies, public schools, and postal systems should procure using a TaaS model on a cost per-mile basis, not for purchasing vehicles (pulling steel).

Investment and Business

The new production system will see a vast reduction in the flow of physical goods and materials through the economy. This will dramatically reduce working capital requirements as physical flows are replaced by capital-free information flows. Likewise, development costs are plunging and, in many cases, could be

Framework Box 8. The Standard Model of Disruption: A New Heuristic at the Limits of Physics and Biology

All sectors of the economy will be disrupted over the next decade and the pace of disruption is likely to accelerate in the 2030s. The Seba Technology Disruption Framework allows for the analysis of disruptions in fundamental sectors of the economy, but policymakers, investors, businesses, or civic leaders may have to make decisions that affect sectors they may not be intimately familiar with. Here is a heuristic to help.

» The building blocks of the new production system will be the bit (and later qbit), photon, electron, molecule, and DNA (or gene). These building blocks are available and plentiful everywhere and can be recombined in infinite ways to create new products and services at essentially zero cost. Information technology will dominate the system of production, but information needs to be embodied in matter and energy. Building blocks that are more powerful, lighter, and faster are superior to those that are less (or similarly) powerful, slower, and heavier. Bits and photons will disrupt electrons, which will disrupt atoms and molecules. Photons are more powerful but orders-of-magnitude lighter and faster than electrons, which are as powerful but orders-of-magnitude lighter and faster than atoms. Similarly, when creating molecules (food, materials, and medicines), manipulating DNA at the micro-organism level allows for the faster production of molecules, with a far lighter production infrastructure and higher degree of precision and accuracy than manipulating a macro-organism. The following are examples of a bits, photons, electrons, atoms, molecules, and DNA (BPEAMD) heuristic:

- For transportation: Electric vehicles (electrons) disrupt ICE vehicles (atoms). Any investments in the ICE vehicle value chain including pipelines, refineries, and gas stations will be stranded.
- For energy and transportation: Solar (photons) disrupts fossil fuels (atoms) and battery electric energy storage (electrons) disrupts centralized fossil fuels (atoms). Any investments in the fossil fuel value chain including pipelines, refineries, and gas stations will be stranded.
- For transportation and infrastructure: Developing high-definition mapping and localization infrastructure will make existing roads dramatically more efficient, so there may be no need to build new roads (bits beat atoms). Autonomous vehicles will drive much of the day, so 90% of parking will be redundant (bits beat atoms).
- For food, healthcare, and materials: Designing molecules (such as proteins and lipids) using Food-as-Software (bits) and producing them via a lighter, faster, local PF infrastructure using micro-organisms (DNA), beats macro-organisms (such as cows and pigs) that need vast amounts of land (atom), fossil fertilizer (atom), and factory farming (atom).

Consider prioritizing investments based on this new standard model of disruption. A heuristic should not replace in-depth sector analysis. But the blunt instruments of the industrial order will be disrupted quickly, enabled by far superior capabilities to manipulate matter, energy, and information with ever greater speed, scale, and precision. This process will accelerate as we achieve even higher technological capabilities closer to the limits of physics and biology.

largely open source. Thus, capital will mainly be required for the roll-out of physical assets (e.g. solar, batteries, and food and goods production centers), not for development and working capital. Financing the roll out of this new system will require major adaptions to our financial system.

» **Create new funding mechanisms that recognize changes in capital requirements**. The capital required will be a mix of debt and equity, with returns underpinned by the offtake of production. Creating new funding mechanisms and driving capital towards them to incentivize investment in the physical infrastructure and value chains required to scale up the new system will be critical. Infrastructure-style financing mechanisms with separate layers of risk and return could be repurposed to provide funding at smaller scale.

» **Use pensions and savings to help build out the new system.** The fixed return profile of these investments (such as distributed power networks, food production centers, and TaaS) will closely match the liability profile of pension schemes (much more so than traditional pension portfolios) and are a good proxy for the ultimate needs for which pensions are designed to meet (such as food, housing, energy, and transportation). Consider changes to rules to drive pension assets and savings towards these products. This would provide a stepping stone towards distributed, participatory ownership (or a new social contract based on a 'right' to energy and other needs) and potentially avoid the fundamental restructuring of the pension systems in Western economies that is inevitable under the current system.

» **Set up simple regulations for individuals to invest in new infrastructure.** Existing regulations (such as Investment Tax Credits) are geared to a system where big finance, corporations, and wealthy individuals invest big money in a few big projects. Society needs participatory finance where every individual can invest directly in smaller projects in their communities, cities, and regions.

- **Develop new legal mechanisms/asset classes** so individuals can invest in small (residential, commercial, and industrial) solar and battery projects and A-EVs, which are cash-generating assets. Preferably, these should be digital-only mechanisms with real-time reporting and fast and direct cash disbursement to investors, municipalities (taxes), and suppliers. To increase trust in these new mechanisms, consider requiring triple-entry accounting. This would minimize the likelihood of accounting fraud as well as legacy credit rating and auditing bias.
- **Make distributed solar, wind, and battery storage projects REIT-able.** This would make trillions of dollars managed by Real Estate Investment Trusts available to scale up the new distributed, robust, clean energy infrastructure.
- **Extend Master Limited Partnerships to solar, wind, and battery projects.** This would make hundreds of billions (potentially trillions) of dollars from public markets available to clean energy projects.

» **Avoid investments in old system infrastructure that will become obsolete.** Capital investments in legacy systems will be stranded. These include investments in the value chain of fossil fuels (mining, pipelines, and refineries), ICE vehicles (supply chain, manufacturing, and distribution), and industrial agriculture (farms, processing plants, and machinery). For example, the UK government is planning to spend £100bn on a high-speed rail link that will be obsolete before it is finished (early 2030s) when it could, for example, repurpose two lanes of highway that will no longer be needed to run autonomous electric road trains for a fraction of the cost (the technology for this is already good enough).

- **Do not use taxpayers or ratepayer money to invest in legacy projects.** Over the foreseeable future, utilities will push for taxpayers to fund power plants (coal, natural gas, oil, and nuclear) under linear assumptions (such as high utilization rates for several decades). These capital investments are already stranded or will be over the next few years. Utilities should instead ask their shareholders to fund these legacy projects. If they are not good enough for shareholders, they are certainly not good enough for ratepayers.

» **Do not make static, long-term investment assumptions.** Infrastructure investments in the 20th century were made under the assumption of long-term system equilibrium. Widescale disruption means this assumption no longer holds. We can no longer assume that a natural gas or coal power plant will be competitive in 10 or even five years. A 25-year NPV calculation will certainly be wrong. For example, you cannot assume a high plant-utilization rate in the future. As there is higher penetration of zero-marginal-cost solar, wind, and storage, legacy power plants will enter a vicious cycle as they are pushed into the role of peakers – the market for them will diminish dramatically so the price needed to sustain them will rise, decreasing the market further.

» **Do not make resale value assumptions based on legacy trends.** For example, ICE vehicle lease agreements assume a certain resale value based on historic prices. This assumption can no longer be made. A more realistic assumption for any ICE vehicles sold today (with an average five-or-more-year lease) is that residual value will be zero or even negative. This will cause a collapse in the value of debt secured on these assets (including cars, equipment, and power infrastructure), which will in turn cause a death spiral for these industries as the cost of purchasing these new assets shoots up (lower residual value = higher monthly payments).

» **Prioritize investments** based on the idea that everything (houses, vehicles, infrastructure, and people) will be connected to information networks. This means that everything should be thought of as a connected, smart device.

» **Mitigate disincentives to investment in markets with deflating prices**. For example, guarantee recovery of investment for the installation of zero-marginal-cost technologies such as solar, wind, and storage.

Manage the Decline of the Old Production System

Ensure the influence of incumbent business is checked and the adverse consequences of the wind-down of these industries are mitigated.

» **Remove direct and indirect incentives and support** through fiscal, regulatory, and legal frameworks. Resist bailouts of industries. For example, remove subsidies and protection currently given to fossil fuel and nuclear industries.

» **Protect people, not businesses**. Allow unviable incumbent businesses to go bankrupt, but protect people through policies to retrain, financial and healthcare support, and access to social capital through the transition. Also create mobility to help people move to different locations with better job and quality-of-life opportunities.

- Create debt-relief programs to help small businesses, individuals, and others within the value chain to exit their incumbent industries.
- Expand social safety-net programs to ensure that individuals affected by disruption can either retrain for or transition to other livelihoods, or retire with dignity.
- Anticipate that whole towns and regions will be disproportionally affected by disruption and enable programs to help local populations transition successfully to the new system. This includes providing educational, financial, healthcare, and social-capital support, as well as creating new employment opportunities.

» **Salvage critical assets of incumbent businesses still required** while the new system is being built (such as power stations, mines, and farms). For example, temporarily, selectively, and minimally subsidize critical legacy fossil fuel-based generation capacity (as it becomes uneconomic) to bridge to the new system. No new fossil or nuclear is needed so resist the misleading push to subsidize natural gas or other energy sources to 'bridge' to the future.

» **Do not lock into long-term price contracts for legacy infrastructure.** For example, as centralized fossil fuel-based energy collapses, commit only to short-term offtake agreements if necessary to keep the lights on.

» **Remove or resist the fightback from incumbent industries** and mindsets in the form of phony science, lobbying (regulatory capture), and disingenuous demands to protect jobs and influence public opinion when they really seek to protect their own financial position.

» **Recognize that this process is deflationary** and that high levels of debt will cause industries to collapse fast, which will have impacts far beyond the industries themselves. Central banks, governments, and investors will need to plan for a long period of supply-side deflation in the foundational sectors, just as there has been deflation in information technologies.

» **Break up the monopoly utility model** in the same way telecom monopolies were broken up (which enabled the internet to break through). Large-scale generation, transmission, distribution, and retail should be separate companies in a given market. The electricity distribution company business model should be to maintain and upgrade poles and system stability (storage) and make money mostly on electricity trade transactions (like eBay or Uber). In an open, transparent, well-designed marketplace, companies will prioritize local generation because it will be cheaper.

» **Break up gas and electric power businesses** (transmission, pipelines, and retail). This will create competition between gas and electric power.

Enabling a New Organizing System

As we have seen, the creation-based system of production will not be adequately managed by our existing Organizing System. The challenge is to both patch up our existing system and do what we can to build robustness over the next decade so we delay its collapse as long as possible, while at the same time creating the conditions for its replacement to emerge. Given the emergent nature of the coevolutionary process of change, we cannot plan exactly what a successful Organizing System will look like, but we can create the conditions and understand the principles that will allow it to emerge.

Patching up the Old System

Ensuring social stability will be critical, a challenge made harder by profound changes to the workforce. Communicating a clear vision for the future (what it looks like and how we get there) will help create support and remove the incentive to look backwards for populist solutions. But more critical is a clear plan to mitigate the adverse consequences of change, which include job losses, increasing instability, and uncertainty. While RethinkX analysis suggests there will be in aggregate job creation during the roll-out phase of the new production system (particularly in building the electric power system), many of the jobs created will require different skills and be in different locations to those lost. Furthermore, as the expansion of the new production system slows, many of these jobs will disappear. This dynamic will allow us to bridge to the world of 'rights' and a new social contract but will contribute to instability. Choices can be made to create additional jobs both to mitigate negative impacts and to accelerate improvements in other areas. For example, the land freed from the disruption of animal farming could be reforested, helping to replace jobs lost in farming in the same areas.

» **Subsidize universal access to information network connectivity, TaaS, and distributed electric power,** including the elderly, less able bodied, the poor, and those living in rural areas.

» **Enable universal access to lifelong education.** America once innovated by creating the land-grant college program, which enabled the emergence of the state university system. In the 2020s, we will need a new universal, lifelong, decentralized, and participatory education-for-all system. To this end, begin the process of developing a new system of education that recognizes the full range of future needs and possibilities.

Recognize short-term requirements (for example for engineers and coders) but realize that these needs will change rapidly. Allow experimentation with new non-traditional forms of delivery that could massively reduce cost and deliver a better service. Decouple quality of education from zip codes.

Enabling the New System

- **Decentralize and experiment at the edge.** Allow states and cities far greater autonomy in decision-making, including areas such as immigration policy, taxation, currency, asset classes, ownership structures, intellectual property, representation and decision-making, education, public expenditures and investment, laws, and regulations.
- **Ensure the center does not crush the edge.** The new Organizing System will represent an existential threat to incumbent interests, including nation states. Breakthrough will only be achieved if the center facilitates and embraces its own transformation and the eventual diminution of its own importance. While increased centralization to nation states is inevitable in the short-term, for us to succeed the center will need to diminish. Indeed this process is inevitable – as the new system emerges in a U.S. state or in Israel, Dubai, Singapore, Mumbai or elsewhere, the role of the federal government will shift profoundly. While its eventual role will depend on the Organizing Systems that emerge at the state or regional levels, the center is likely to become a collaborator not director, continually contributing to the network to create value.
- **Put systems thinking at the center of all scenario-planning and decision-making.** While recognizing the shortcomings implicit in modeling future scenarios, be prepared to update assumptions and change course rapidly.
- **Focus governance and decision-making on principles of resilience, adaptivity, flexibility, and agility.** Encourage novel approaches and embrace the lessons of experiment failure.
- **Be aware that a new social contract will be required,** which might grant a right to needs (increasing over time as costs drop), while redefining concepts like work, reward, and purpose. A gradual transition will be required as society nears the end of the scale-up of the new system and jobs (as we define them today) disappear. Concepts like a universal basic income that, over time, will become rapidly more affordable, and the pension reforms discussed above, can help bridge the transition.
- **Plan early for massive change to land use and the built environment.** The simultaneous disruption of the foundational sectors will create extraordinary new possibilities for towns and cities and well as farming regions. Cities of far greater density and size will be feasible (manageable cities of 100m people will be possible by the early 2030s), as will far more distributed conurbations of almost limitless scale, as the cluster effect favoring cities diminishes and land is freed from food production and transportation. Furthermore, demands for land within and around cities will change as food production, goods manufacturing, and energy production decentralize and the transportation system radically changes in land-use requirements. There will be many competing interests for these areas and it is essential that regions begin to plan early, taking full account of all potential future uses.
- **Develop rules of the network and govern at the point of connection.** As governance moves away from our current centralized, hierarchical structures, new structures will emerge at the level of the node (localized, self-sufficient community) and the network (far broader and ultimately global). Developing the rules of the network will be critical. This will not require global agreement, as the 'best-fit' Organizing System, wherever it emerges, is likely to spread rapidly as it outcompetes all others. Connection to the network will be vital to participate in any aspect of society and thus governing at the point of connection will be critical. Regions that hope to lead will need to focus on these network principles that will allow the new system of production to be managed and governed effectively.
- **Develop verifiable and immutable methods to establish trust** across the network for all forms of institutions and human relationships.
- **Develop principles for usage and control of AI and biotechnology.** Both AI and biotechnologies have the potential to create extraordinary opportunities for humanity, but as the cost and accessibility of both plummet, so the risks of rogue individuals or groups harnessing them for negative means rise. AI is likely to be integrated into decision-making across society, including in the allocation of scarce resources (market function) and policy decisions (democracy). Furthermore, AI will have a critical role across all aspects of the production and Organizing Systems, so creating clear principles that help mitigate the risks of adverse outcomes will be critical. A modern form of the Philadelphia convention, to decide on these principles and decide on what humanity should optimize for, might be needed.

Glossary

This glossary provides definitions for both new terms that we introduce in this book, as well as existing terms that we use in an unconventional way.

Technology

The application of knowledge to manipulate matter, energy, and information – the basic constituents of the physical world – for useful purpose.

Technological Capability

A measure of the speed, scale, and precision with which we can manipulate matter, energy, and information with technology. Can be evaluated in absolute terms of what is achievable, as well as in relative terms of what is feasible at a given cost (note that cost includes all resources used, not only financial costs).

Technological Progress

Improvement in technological capability. Can apply in either absolute terms of what is achievable (i.e. greater power) or in relative terms of what is feasible at a given cost (i.e. greater efficiency). Over time, this manifests as the ability to do more with less.

Technology Disruption

A disruption happens when new products or services create a new market and significantly weaken, transform or destroy existing product categories, markets, or industries. Disruptions are made possible by the convergence of technologies and business model innovations enabled by these technologies.

Disruptions can occur in four ways:

- **From above:** A new technology is initially superior and more expensive than incumbent products or services, but rapidly becomes cheaper at a faster rate, while improving performance.
- **From below:** A new technology is initially inferior and less expensive than incumbent products or services, but rapidly becomes superior while decreasing costs at a faster rate.
- **Architectural:** A new technology radically changes the way a product or service is produced, managed, distributed, or sold.
- **Big bang:** A new technology offers both superior performance and lower cost at launch.

Incumbent businesses are often wiped out and replaced by new, dominant enterprises offering new products and/or services and/or business models.

Disruptions can cause substantial changes to an entire sector, the impacts of which ripple out through other sectors, the wider economy, and society.

Production System

The basic character of humanity's relationship with the natural world and its resources, mediated by technology, for the purpose of meeting the full range of human needs (and wants). Three major modes of production – foraging, extraction, and creation – define the ages of humanity.

Organizing System

The Organizing System encompasses the prevailing models of thought, belief systems, myths, values, abstractions, and conceptual frameworks that help explain how the world works and our relationship to it, in any given society. It comprises the political, social, and economic systems, including the governing structures, institutions, and culture, that oversee, influence, and manage society and provide the incentives (compulsion and reward) that drive the decisions, actions, and beliefs of individuals and groups.

At a sector level, it manifests as the rules and regulations, metrics, business models and value chain, incentive structures and drivers, and organizing principles.

Societal Capabilities

A measure of the structural complexity, resource management, productivity output, and quality of life for its population that a society can sustain over time given the prevailing production and Organizing Systems.

Foundational Sectors

The five sectors of the global economy that directly manipulate matter, energy, and information to serve basic human needs: information, energy, transportation, food, and materials.

Age

A period where the fundamental drivers and structure of the production system – that influence both the coevolution of the production and Organizing Systems and human behavior – remain broadly constant. The Age of Foraging represents Humanity 1.0. The Age of Extraction represents Humanity 2.0. Humanity now has the potential to enter the Age of Freedom (Humanity 3.0).

Order

Within an age, an order represents a broadly constant societal capability frontier (see below) set by the combination of technological and organizing capabilities. A new order represents an order-of-magnitude improvement in technological capabilities with material adaptions to the Organizing System, leading to a new societal capability frontier.

Wave

Within an order, a wave represents a broadly constant sector capability frontier set by the combination of technological and organizing capabilities within a foundational sector. A sector capability frontier is generally defined by its value chain (infrastructure, supply and distribution chains, business model, metrics, and reward systems). A new wave represents a disruption to one of these sectors and an order-of-magnitude increase in technological capabilities with a new value chain and sector-level Organizing System, within a materially stable societal Organizing System. The steam engine and internal combustion engine represent waves.

Capability Frontier

The maximum capabilities that can be achieved given the prevailing combination of production and Organizing Systems. At a sector level, this manifests as a technological frontier – the maximum potential technological capabilities that can be achieved given the technologies, value chains, and business models that are prevalent within the wave. At a civilization level, this manifests as a societal capability frontier – the maximum potential societal capabilities that can be achieved given the combination of the Organizing System and the technologies available within an order.

Dark Age

A period where prevailing societal capabilities fall substantially below the societal capability frontier. A dark age manifests as a reversal of social complexity, an ability to support a far smaller population, and a lower quality of life.

Rupture Point

The point at which a system is forced out of its equilibrium state.

Possibility Space

The set of potential future pathways for a system at any point in time. When a system is in equilibrium, these can represent a narrow band of possibilities. When a convergence of factors pushes the system out of equilibrium, the range of possibilities can diverge dramatically.

Linear Possibility Space

The possibility space that appears when viewed through a narrow, linear mindset. This mindset that assumes that the future will differ only marginally from the present, and that linear extrapolation of recent trends provides an accurate guide for the pathways ahead, ignoring the potential for non-linear change that manifests in all complex systems.

Fractal

Fractals are complex patterns that are self-similar across scales. There is a fractal quality to patterns of change in human systems: ages, orders, waves, and sectors.

Emergence

A process by which a system of interacting building blocks of individuals, technologies, and earth resources (matter, energy and information) gives rise to a new system with properties, rules and behaviors that cannot be understood or predicted by a mechanistic linear addition of their individual properties or contributions. For instance, a human being cannot be understood or predicted from the chemical properties of carbon, hydrogen, nitrogen, calcium, phosphorus and other elements that make up the human body.

Attractor

A state where the system can be in equilibrium. While there can be an infinite number of potential states, the number of attractors is likely to be small. For instance, mathematically, combining DNA, RNA and proteins would allow for an infinite variety of life forms. However, all species on earth fall under one of three types of life forms: archaea, bacteria and eukaryote. For a civilization, an attractor is a state where the technologies / production system and organizing system are a fit (mutually adapted).

Robustness

The system's ability to operate and maintain its organization and function within a wide range of states including perturbations and shocks. A system's ability to operate relatively independently of inputs from its surroundings.

Resilience

The systems ability to recover and bounce back from perturbations and shocks.

Appendix 1 Seba Technology Disruption Framework

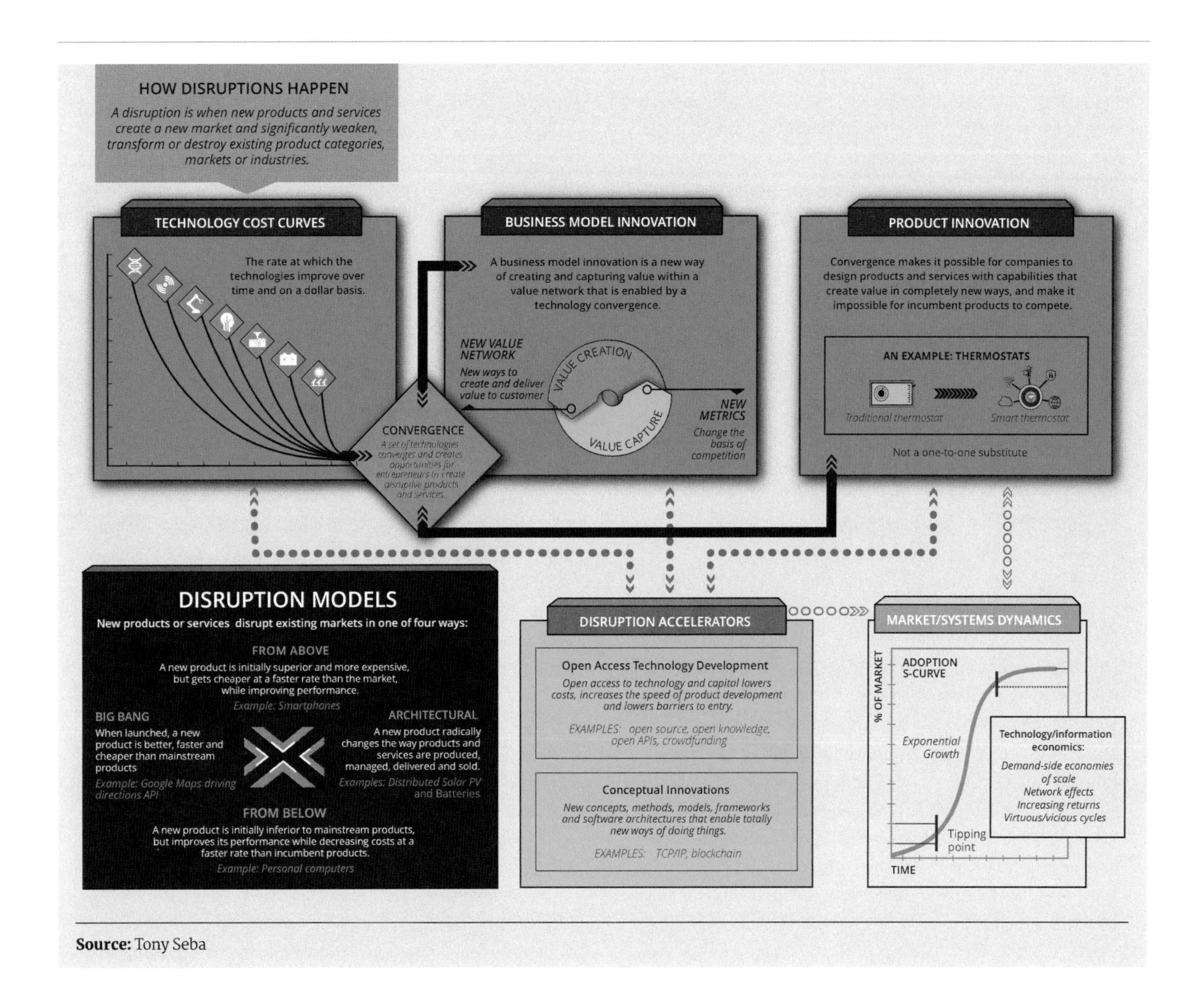

Source: Tony Seba

Notes

1 Capabilities can be thought of across many dimensions. For example, improvement in computer processing is usually measured in number of transistors per unit of space (inch). But these transistors also improve in speed, so improvement in processing power is a combination of both. Size, speed, and also durability are all relevant measures. Lithium-ion batteries improve in cost/kWh stored, but also in energy density, charge times, and lifetime. While the cost curve measures only $/unit of storage – the other measures of capability are also relevant. A cheap battery that is huge, for example, would be of no use for a smartphone.

2 Fiegerman, S. (2012, June 29). The Experts Speak: Here's What People Predicted Would Happen When The iPhone Came Out... *Business Insider.*

3 Lieberman, D. (2007, April 30). CEO Forum: Microsoft's Ballmer having a "great time." *USA Today.*

4 Marsel, K. (July 30, 2007). Analyst: iPhone is Harry Potter "squib" of cell phones. *AppleInsider.*

5 Dormehl, L. (2017, June 26). "Apple should pull the plug": 10 iPhone predictions from 2007. *Cult of Mac.*

6 Mainstream analysts and consultants should have learned from the recent major telecoms disruption. When hired by AT&T (then the largest telecoms company in the world) in 1985 to predict the size of the mobile market by the year 2000, McKinsey came back with an estimate of 900,000. The number was 120 million. It was out by a factor of 120. The consultant was not alone. Vinod Khosla, the Silicon Valley investor, looked at forecasts by major technology research consultancies between 2002 and 2010 and found they routinely underestimated growth in the mobile phone market by a factor of eight.

7 Gupta, R. (2016, May 9). Nokia CEO ended his speech saying: "We didn't do anything wrong, but somehow we lost". *LinkedIn.*

8 Macrotrends. (2020). Apple Market Cap 2006-2020 | AAPL.

9 Statista. (2013, July 25). Global market share held by Nokia smartphones from 1st quarter 2007 to 2nd quarter 2013 [Data File].

10 Statista. (2020, February 27). Nokia's Net Sales 1999-2019 [Data File].

11 Rosenfeld, M. J., Thomas, R. J., & Hausen, S. (2019). Disintermediating your friends: How online dating in the United States displaces other ways of meeting. *Proceedings of the National Academy of Sciences, 116(36)*, 17753–17758.

12 Carson, B. (2017, April 14). Uber booked $20 billion in rides in 2016, but it's still losing billions. *Business Insider.*

13 Damodaran, A. (2014, June 18). Uber Isn't Worth $17 Billion. *FiveThirtyEight.*

14 Shahan, Z. (2020, January 19). Tesla Model 3 = 7th Best Selling Car In USA. *Clean Technica.*

15 United States Department of Commerce and Labor. (1909). *Statistical Abstract of the United States, Table 224: Prices of Domestic Iron.* Washington D.C.: Government Printing Office.

16 Bramley, A (2015, December 3). How Chicago's Slaughterhouse Spectacles Paved The Way For Big Meat. *NPR.*

17 The 1885 Otto engine had a mass/power ratio of 270 g/W while the 1908 Ford Model T had a mass/power ratio of 5 g/W, an improvement of 54x.
Smil, V. (2013). *Making the Modern World: Materials and Dematerialization.* Hoboken, New Jersey: John Wiley & Sons.

18 Gross, D. (1997). *Forbes: Greatest Business Stories of All Time: 20 Inspiring Tales of Entrepreneurs Who Changed the Way We Live and Do Business.* Hoboken, New Jersey: John Wiley & Sons.

19 RethinkX estimate.

20 Calder, L. (2001). *Financing the American Dream: A Cultural History of Consumer Credit.* Princeton, New Jersey: Princeton University Press.

21 Jakle, J. A., & Sculle, K. A. (1994). *The Gas Station in America.* Baltimore, Maryland: John Hopkins University Press.

22 Jamal, H. (2017, January 22). Road Construction Machinery – Uses of Road Construction Tools and Equipment. *About Civil.*

23 U.S. Advisory Commission on Intergovernmental Relations. (1995, September). Significant Features of Fiscal Federalism: Budget Processes and Tax Systems (Report No. M-197). Washington D.C.: USACIR.

24 Kinney, T. A. (2004). *The Carriage Trade: Making Horse-Drawn Vehicles in America.* Baltimore, Maryland: Johns Hopkins University Press.

25 Long, W. (1903, August 4). "New Bills: Motor-Cars Bill (Lords)". UK Parliament. House of Commons. *Hansard.* 4(126).

26 Carriage Association of America. (1904, April). The Carriage Monthly. (40). Philadelphia, Pennsylvania: Ware Brothers Publishing.

27 Carriage Association of America. (1912, December). *The Future of the Horse Vehicle.* The Carriage Monthly. (48). Philadelphia, Pennsylvania: Ware Brothers Publishing. From Kinney, T. A. (2004). *The Carriage Trade: Making Horse-Drawn Vehicles in America.* Baltimore, Maryland: Johns Hopkins University Press.

28 Edwards, A. (1943, June 30). *Sixteenth Census of the United States: 1940, Comparative Occupation Statistics for the United States 1870-1930.* Washington D.C.: United States Government Printing Office.

29 Smil, V. (2013). *Making the Modern World: Materials and Dematerialization.* Hoboken, New Jersey: John Wiley & Sons.

30 Donlan, T. G. (2008, May 8). A World of Wealth: How Capitalism Turns Profits Into Progress. Upper Saddle River, New Jersey: Financial Times Press.

31 Kinney, T. A. (2004). *The Carriage Trade: Making Horse-Drawn Vehicles in America.* Baltimore, Maryland: Johns Hopkins University Press.

32 Edwards, A. (1943, June 30). *Sixteenth Census of the United States: 1940, Comparative Occupation Statistics for the United States 1870-1930.* Washington D.C.: United States Government Printing Office.

33 Olmstead, A. L., & Rhode, P. W. (2001). Reshaping the Landscape: The Impact and Diffusion of the Tractor in American Agriculture, 1910-1960. *The Journal of Economic History, 61(3),* 663-698. JSTOR.

34 In another reinforcing feedback loop, thanks to federal and military incentives, 83% of U.S. population growth in the 1950s and 1970s took place in the suburbs as the suburban population grew from 36 million to 74 million people.
Jackson, K. (1987, April 16). *Crabgrass Frontier: The Suburbanization of the United States.* Oxford, United Kingdom: Oxford University Press. Quoted from Poleg, D. (2019, October 31). Rethinking Real Estate: A Roadmap to Technology's Impact on the World's Largest Asset Class. New York, New York: Palgrave Macmillan.
Also, here:
Locke, J. L., & Wright, B. (2019). *The American Yawp: A Massively Collaborative Open U.S. History Textbook. The Affluent Society, II: Rise of the Suburbs* (Vol. 2). Palo Alto, California: Stanford University Press.

35 Nicolaides, B., & Wiese, A. (2017). Suburbanization in the United States after 1945. *Oxford Research Encyclopedias, American History.*

36 According to the American Automobile Association, there were more than 2,000 free car camps by 1924. The same year, a single camp in Yellowstone National Park received over 100,000 auto campers, according to the National Park Service. *The Chicago Tribune* predicted in 1929 that more than 5 million Americans would camp with their automobiles that year.
Henderson, L. (2010). America's Roadside Lodging: The Rise and Fall of the Motel. *Historia, 19,* 23-43.

37 Craven, W. F., & Cate, J. L. (1984). *The Army Air Forces in World War II: Men and Planes* (Vol. 6). Chicago, Illinois: University of Chicago Press.

38 Ford built 6,790 B-24 bombers, 282,354 Jeeps, and 42,676 Army/Navy Cargo Trucks. It also produced 13,893 Universal Carriers for British Commonwealth nations.
Jackson, D. (2020, February 27). Ford Motor Car Company in World War Two. *US Auto Industry World War Two.*

39 Linear forecasts, which ignore feedbacks and assume "all else remains equal," are not credible representations of future possibilities. The scenarios they depict are not plausible and we urge readers confronted by them to be duly skeptical.

40 The migration of Greek intellectuals to Europe (especially Italy) in the years between the Sack of Constantinople (1204) and the Ottoman Conquest of Constantinople (1453) was essential to the discovery and revival of Greek and Roman studies that led to the European Renaissance in humanism and science.
How did the Fall of Constantinople change the Renaissance in Italy? *Daily History.*

41 Byrne, J. P. (2017). *The World of Renaissance Italy.* Santa Barbara, California: ABC-CLIO.

42 Examples of direct influence abound. John Argyropoulos's students included Leonardo da Vinci, Piero di Cosimo de' Medici, and Lorenzo de' Medici, while Johann Reuchlin and Barlam of Seminara taught Petrarch. Copernicus learned from the writings of Besilius Bessarion.
Matula, J. (2006). John Argyropoulos and his Importance for the Latin West. *Philosophica,* (7).
Hay, D. (1961) *The Italian Renaissance in its Historical Background.* Cambridge, United Kingdom: Cambridge University Press.
Goddu, A. (2010, January 25). *Copernicus and the Aristotelian Tradition Education, Reading, and Philosophy in Copernicus's Path to Heliocentrism.* Leiden, Netherlands: Brill.

43 The first printed book was found in China dating from 868 CE.
Daley, J. (2016, May 11). Five Things to Know About the Diamond Sutra, the World's Oldest Dated Printed Book. *Smithsonian Magazine.*

44 For example, Christopher Columbus, a sailor from Genoa, became an explorer in Lisbon and, after being turned down by he kings of Portugal, France, and England, got funding from the queen and king of Castile, León, and Aragon (Spain) to sail West to bring back spices, gold, and silk from Asia.
Mach, A. (2011, October 10). Christopher Columbus: Five things you thought you knew about the explorer. *Christian Science Monitor.*

45 Kurlansky, M. (2016). Paper: *Paging Through History.* New York, New York: W. W. Norton & Company.

46 Kovarik, B. (2015). *Revolutions in Communication: Media History from Gutenberg to the Digital Age.* New York, New York: Bloomsbury Publishing USA.

47 Ibid.

48 Ibid.

49 The Editors of Encyclopaedia Britannica. Mainz. *Encyclopaedia Britannica.*

50 Kurlansky, M. (2016). Paper: *Paging Through History.* New York, New York: W. W. Norton & Company.
51 Some of the first books printed in the French language were thanks in large part to German talent fleeing violence. Tucker, D. H., Unwin, P. S., & Unwin, G. (2017, November 15). History of publishing – The age of early printing: 1450–1550. *Encyclopaedia Britannica.*
52 Chase-Dunn, C., & Lerro, B. (2013). Social Change: *Globalization from the Stone Age to the Present.* Abingdon, United Kingdom: Routledge.
53 For example, an amendment to the constitution, a change in monetary system from the gold standard to fiat money, or an expansion of democratic representation to women or minorities.
54 The Mysterious World. Top 9 Most Amazing Cave Paintings.
55 Tellier, L.-N. (2009). *Urban World History: An Economic and Geographical Perspective.* New York, New York. Springer International Publishing.
56 Kane, S. (2016, March 18). The human race once came dangerously close to dying out – here's how it changed us. *Business Insider.*
57 Scott, J. C. (2017). *Against the Grain: A Deep History of the Earliest States* (1 edition). New Haven, Connecticut: Yale University Press.
58 Ibid.
59 The scale of breakdown depends on the complexity and scale of the society. Simple early civilizations in the Fertile Crescent did not have far to fall (relatively speaking) – the region could support a number of independent proto-cities, so while an individual city might collapse, others of similar capabilities continued to function. As civilizations grew, there was less scope for regions to support multiple civilizations in this way.
60 There is plenty of literature that deals with the collapse of civilizations. Two of the best are *Collapse* by Jared Diamond and *The Great Disruption* by Paul Gilding.
61 After Rome's collapse, several cities (like Baghdad, Hangzhou, and Beijing) achieved Roman Order societal capabilities (in terms of a city size of one million people).
62 Morris, I. (2011). *Why the West Rules – for Now: The Patterns of History and What They Reveal About the Future.* London, United Kingdom: Picador.
63 Ibid.
64 Mark, J. J. (2019, September 20). Bronze Age Collapse. Ancient History Encyclopedia.
65 Morris, I. (2011). *Why the West Rules – for Now: The Patterns of History and What They Reveal About the Future.* London, United Kingdom: Picador.
66 Taagepera, R. (1979). Size and Duration of Empires: Growth-Decline Curves, 600 B.C. to 600 A.D. *Social Science History, 3(3/4),* 115–138.
67 Schwartz, R. K. (2004, October). All Roads Led to Rome: Roman Food Production in North Africa. *Repast, 4,* 5–9.
68 Morris, I. (2011). *Why the West Rules – for Now: The Patterns of History and What They Reveal About the Future.* London, United Kingdom: Picador.
69 Frankopan, P. (2015, August 27). *The Silk Roads: A New History of the World.* Oxford, United Kingdom: Bloomsbury Publishing.
70 Ibid.
71 Rockström, J., Steffen, W., Noone, K., Persson, Å., Chapin, F. S. I., Lambin, E. F., Lenton, T. M., ... & Foley, J. (2009). Planetary Boundaries: Exploring the Safe Operating Space for Humanity. *Ecol Soc,* 14(2).
72 For example, Coca-Cola is available in every country except North Korea and Cuba.
De Luce, I. (2019, August 13). Coca-Cola is sold in all but 2 countries on Earth. Here's what their ads look like around the world. *Business Insider Malaysia.*
73 Levinson, M. (2008). *The Box: How the Shipping Container Made the World Smaller and the World Economy Bigger.* Princeton, New Jersey: Princeton University Press.
74 Ibid.
75 World Shipping Council. (2019, July). Top 50 World Container Ports.
76 In 2019, Amazon marketplace had three million active sellers with a gross merchandise value exceeding $200 billion. 42% of the active sellers across all sixteen global Amazon marketplaces are based in China, up from 26% in 2017. Marketplace Pulse. (2019, December 16). Marketplaces Year in Review 2019.
77 In 2019, new wind and solar installation made up around 64% of total annual power capacity expansion globally. International Renewable Energy Agency. (2020, March 31). Renewable Capacity Highlights.
78 Hansen, S. (2020, March 26). The Rise and Fall of General Electric (GE). *Investopedia.*
79 Iron Matrix. (2019). Why We're Different.
80 Governance and communities may be able to operate in multiple dimensions. No longer constrained by the limitations of transportation or information technologies, we are already seeing virtual communities begin to develop globally in many dimensions, brought together by shared interests and values.
81 British Library. Overview. *East India Company.*
Blakemore, E. (2019, September 6) How the East India Company became the world's most powerful business. *National Geographic.*

82 Center for Responsible Politics. Elections Overview: Did Money Win? OpenSecrets.org.

83 This is not to say we will willingly abandon the concept of countries, but rather they will not be the most effective form of governance and risk being outcompeted by new governance structures that better enable progress.

84 For example, Silicon Valley used to be geographically bound but has evolved into a worldwide network of people sharing similar beliefs and interests.

85 Rouleau, G. (2016, April 1). Simulating The 2016 Baseball Season. *MathWorks.*

86 Although in a complex system, of course, it will be both to some degree.

87 Elkington, J., Lim, J., & Smith, L. (2016). Breakthrough Business Models: Exponentially more social, lean, integrated and circular. *Volans; Business and Sustainable Development Commission.*

88 Scott, J. C. (2017). *Against the Grain: A Deep History of the Earliest States* (1 edition). New Haven, Connecticut: Yale University Press.

89 Ibid.

90 RethinkX calculation.

91 Harari, Y. N. (2017). *Homo Deus: A Brief History of Tomorrow.* London, United Kingdom: Harvill Secker.

92 Bouratinos, E. (2018). *Science, Objectivity, and Consciousness.* Princeton, New Jersey: ICRL Press.

93 A NetCorp or NetLC would be new network-based legal entities. Company names are imagined. Any resemblance with existing corporations is purely accidental.

94 Rodgers, D. T. The Progressive Era to the New Era, 1900–1929. *The Gilder Lehrman Institute of American History.*

95 Massaro, R. (2020). 2020 Silicon Valley Index. *Joint Venture Silicon Valley, Institute for Regional Studies.*

96 Even if there are pockets within the leadership that understand the potential, recent political developments in Britain, the U.S., Germany, and other Western powers have shown how powerful resistance to immigration is – even by those benefiting from immigration. As we explain elsewhere, racism, sexism, and xenophobia are core strands of the Extraction Age DNA.

97 Welch, D. & Naughton, K. (2020, April 13). Fear of an Impending Car-Price Collapse Grips Auto Industry. *Bloomberg.*

98 More here: Seba, T. (2018, March 26). Zero emission miles: How to decarbonize road transport quickly and cheaply.

List of Recommended Books

In the process of researching this book, we have read hundreds of books, many of them brilliant but a few have been deeply influential.

We stand on the shoulders of these (and other) authors and heartily recommend our readers to become acquainted with their work. We are both thankful to them for the tremendous value of their work and apologetic if some of the concepts became too embedded in our thinking.

Frankopan, P. (2017). *The Silk Roads: A New History of the World.* Oxford, United Kingdom: Bloomsbury Publishing.

Gilding, P. (2011). *The Great Disruption: Why the Climate Crisis Will Bring On the End of Shopping and the Birth of a New World.* New York, New York: Bloomsbury Press.

Hidalgo, C. A. (2015). *Why Information Grows: The Evolution of Order, from Atoms to Economies.* New York, New York: Basic Books.

Kauffman, S. A. (2019). *A World Beyond Physics: The Emergence and Evolution of Life.* New York, New York: Oxford University Press USA.

Morris, I. (2011). *Why the West Rules – for Now: The Patterns of History and What They Reveal About the Future.* London, United Kingdom: Picador.

Scott, J. C. (2017). *Against the Grain: A Deep History of the Earliest States.* New Haven, Connecticut: Yale University Press.

Strogatz, S. H. (2003). *Sync: The Emerging Science of the Spontaneous Order.* New York, New York: Hachette Books.

West, G. B. (2017). *Scale: The Universal Laws of Growth, Innovation, Sustainability, and the Pace of Life in Organisms, Cities, Economies, and Companies.* New York, New York: Penguin Random House.

Disclaimer

Any findings, predictions, inferences, implications, judgments, beliefs, opinions, recommendations, suggestions, and similar matters in this book are statements of opinion by the authors and are not statements of fact. You should treat them as such and come to your own conclusions based upon your own research. The content of this book does not constitute advice of any kind and you should not take any action or refrain from taking any action in reliance upon this book or the contents thereof.

This book includes possible scenarios selected by the authors. The scenarios are not designed to be comprehensive or necessarily representative of all situations. Any scenario or statement in this book is based upon certain assumptions and methodologies chosen by the authors. Other assumptions and/or methodologies may exist that could lead to other results and/or opinions.

Neither the authors nor publisher of this book, nor any of their respective affiliates, directors, officers, employees, partners, licensors, agents, or representatives provide any financial or investment advice by virtue of publishing and/or distributing this book and nothing in this book should be construed as constituting financial or investment advice of any kind or nature. Neither the authors nor publisher of this book, nor any of their respective affiliates, directors, officers, employees, partners, licensors, agents, or representatives make any recommendation or representation regarding the advisability of purchasing, investing in, or making any financial commitment with respect to any asset, property, and/or business and nothing in this book should be construed as such. A decision to purchase, invest in or make any financial commitment with respect to any such asset, property, and/or business should not be made in reliance on this book or any information contained therein. The general information contained in this book should not be acted upon without obtaining specific legal, tax, and/or investment advice from a licensed professional.

Nothing in this book constitutes an invitation or inducement to engage in investment activity for the purposes of section 21 of the Financial Services and Markets Act 2000. No representations or warranties of any kind or nature, whether express or implied, are given in relation to this book or the information contained therein. The authors and publishers of this book disclaim, to the fullest extent permitted by applicable law, all representations and warranties of any kind or nature, whether express or implied, concerning this book and the contents thereof.

To the fullest extent permitted by applicable law, the authors and publisher of this book and their respective affiliates, directors, officers, employees, partners, licensors, agents, and representatives shall not be liable for:

» any loss or damage suffered or incurred by you or any other person or entity as a result of any action that you or any other person or entity may take, or refrain from taking, as a result of this book or any information contained therein
» any dealings you may have with third parties as a result of this book or any information contained therein
» any loss or damage which you or any other person or entity may suffer or incur as a result of or connected to your, or any other person's or entity's, use of this book or any information contained therein.

In this disclaimer, references to this book include any information provided by the authors or publisher, or any of their respective affiliates, directors, officers, employees, partners, licensors, agents, or representatives that relates to this book, including, without limitation, summaries, press releases, social media posts, interviews, and articles concerning this book.

About the Authors

James Arbib

James Arbib is chairman of a UK-based family investment office with a diversified portfolio across all asset classes and a focus on the risks and opportunities of technology disruption. He is the founder of Tellus Mater, an independent philanthropic foundation dedicated to exploring the impacts of technology and its potential for solving some of the world's most challenging problems.

He is the co-founder of RethinkX and has given keynote speeches at dozens of events including for BlackRock, Goldman Sachs, governments and corporations.

A graduate in history from Trinity College, Cambridge, he has a Masters in Sustainability Leadership, also from Cambridge. He is a qualified chartered accountant and worked as an investment analyst covering utilities.

Tony Seba

Tony Seba is a world-renowned thought leader, author, speaker, educator, angel investor and Silicon Valley entrepreneur. He is the author of the #1 Amazon best-selling book "*Clean Disruption of Energy and Transportation*," "*Solar Trillions*" and "*Winners Take All*," and co-author of "*Rethinking Transportation 2020-2030*" and "*Rethinking Food and Agriculture 2020-2030*".

He has been featured in several movies and documentaries including Bloomberg's Forward Thinking: A Sustainable World, 2040, and SunGanges. He is recipient of many awards including the Savvy Awards (2019), Solar Future Today's Visionary Influencer Award (2018), and Clean Energy Action's 2017 Sunshine Award. He is the creator of the Seba Technology Disruption Framework™. His work focuses on technology disruption, the convergence of technologies, business model innovation, and product innovation that is leading to the disruption of the world's major industries. He has been a keynote speaker at hundreds of global events and organizations including Google, the European Commission, Davos, COP21, CLSA, J.P. Morgan, Nomura, National Governors Association, Conference on World Affairs, the Global Leaders Forum, Intersolar and China EV100. He has taught thousands of entrepreneurs and corporate leaders at Stanford Continuing Studies. He has a Stanford MBA and an MIT degree in Computer Science and Engineering.

Made in the USA
Coppell, TX
08 December 2021